This book is to be returned on or before the last date below.
You may renew the book unless it is requested by another borrower.
You can now renew your books by phone or on-line
visit our website www.libraries.sandwell.gov.uk SN
THANK YOU FOR USING YOUR LIBRARY

Sandwell
Metropolitan Borough Council
Library & Information Service

D0234416

ROSES FOR A LADY

Edith Somerville, great-granddaughter of a wealthy banker in L.A., received two-dozen red roses with a note attached: she would receive one rose less every day and on receipt of the last rose she would die . . . Private Detective Johnny Merak sets out to find the would-be killer and when certain members of the family are murdered, Johnny finds proof of yet another, earlier, murder. But it's not until Edith receives the final rose that the killer is unmasked . . .

JOHN GLASBY

ROSES FOR A LADY

LINFORD
Leicester

First published in Great Britain

First Linford Edition
published 2010

British Library CIP Data

Glasby, John S. (John Stephen)
 Roses for a lady.- -(Linford mystery library)
 1. Merak, Johnny (Fictitous character)- -
 Fiction.
 2. Private investigators- -California- -
 Los Angeles- -Fiction.
 3. Detective and mystery stories
 4. Large type books.
 I. Title II. Series
 823.9'14–dc22

 ISBN 978–1–44480–219–1

Published by
F. A. Thorpe (Publishing)
Anstey, Leicestershire

Set by Words & Graphics Ltd.
Anstey, Leicestershire
Printed and bound in Great Britain by
T. J. International Ltd., Padstow, Cornwall

This book is printed on acid-free paper

1

A Very Strange Meeting

It was late in the afternoon and I was on the train coming back to L.A. I'd just finished a case for a client and was looking forward to getting back home and seeing Dawn again. I'd got myself a seat next to the window but although it still wanted ten minutes for four o'clock in the afternoon, the sky outside was as black as night. We seemed to be running through a dark endless tunnel with little sign of the outside world. This was undoubtedly one of the worst storms I'd ever known. Lightning strokes turned the rain-smeared window into a glittering sheet of tiny diamonds. Thunder hammered at my ears so that the train seemed to shake.

I'd switched on the overhead light and had just put down the book I'd been reading. It was then I noticed the woman

1

a couple of seats in front of me. There were only three other passengers in the compartment and what caught my attention was that she had turned her head and was smiling at me. I tried to recall if I'd seen her before but nothing came to mind. Yet she either knew me or had mistaken me for someone else.

There was something about her smile that intrigued me. It was a lonely, frightened kind of smile, like that of a child sitting in the dark, wondering if anyone would come if they called out. I guessed she was in her mid-forties, neatly dressed. Her left hand clutched the back of her seat and I noticed there was no ring on her finger so I put her down as unmarried. She clearly had something on her mind but wasn't sure whether to do anything about it.

Then she suddenly pushed herself up in her seat, leaned over the back, and said, 'These storms always scare me and it seems to be getting worse. Do you mind if I sit beside you?'

'Not at all,' I said. 'If we're lucky we'll run out of it before we reach L.A.' Had I known then what this chance meeting was going to lead me into I would have tried to ignore her and concentrate on my book. But not having my crystal ball with me at the time I decided to be a gentleman and lifted my book from the seat.

She came and sat down next to me. I could tell she had class and yet there was the impression she'd fallen on hard times. In my business as a private investigator you meet all kinds of people and I'd developed this knack of telling a lot merely from just looking at them.

A particularly loud peal of thunder sounded almost directly over the train and she clutched instinctively at my arm. She drew back as the echoes atrophied into the distance. 'I'm sorry I'm acting this way. I guess I'm making a fool of myself.'

'I can understand,' I told her. I pointed out of the window. 'The sky seems to be getting a bit brighter in that direction.' Pausing for a moment, I asked, 'You're not being followed by anyone, are you?'

Her head jerked up. She stared at me

and there was that look of stark fear in her grey eyes again and this time it had nothing to do with the storm outside.

'Why do you ask that?' she asked. I noticed the tremor in her voice at once.

Taking out my business card, I gave it to her. She read it slowly. 'You're a private detective.'

'That's right. Johnny Merak. I have an office in L.A. I'm on my way back there now. Believe me, I've no wish to pry into your private affairs but I see people like you every day of the week and I can recognize when someone is in big trouble. If you want to tell me about it, I assure you that nothing you tell me will go beyond the two of us.'

I could see she was struggling whether to trust me or not. After all, I was a perfect stranger and anyone could get hold of a business card like mine. She sat staring down at it for a while and then looked up. It was clear she'd made up her mind. 'My name is Edith Somerville, Mister Merak. You may have heard of the Somervilles.'

I had. The name was familiar. I raked

through my mental files of important people in L.A. and the surrounding area. Then I had it. 'The banking family,' I said.

'That's correct. My great grandfather founded it nearly two hundred years ago.'

I sat back in my seat. The continuous clatter of the wheels on the metal rails was a monotonous background to the thoughts that were whirling through my mind at that moment. There had been a lot of rumours concerning this particular family, certain members of which were reputed to have strong links with the Organization.

If any of these rumours were true, I could see that I might be getting myself into very big trouble by helping this woman. The Mobs didn't like anyone, particularly private eyes like Johnny Merak, poking into their affairs. Certainly I'd done favours for Enrico Manzelli the Big Boss who ran all of the Underworld families. But that wouldn't help me if I probed into something they wanted kept quiet.

I realized Edith Somerville was speaking again. 'I can understand you wondering how come a member of the family would be travelling like this.' She indicated the dress and coat she wore which had clearly never seen the inside of any of the big, expensive stores. 'Unfortunately there was a big quarrel a few years ago between my father and his brother Herbert, the senior partner in the business. We're now regarded as the poor relations and very seldom have anything to do with the others, especially since my father died three years ago.'

'Yet none of what you've just told me explains why you're so obviously terrified,' I said pointedly.

'No, I guess it doesn't.' She bit her lower lip. 'But what's happened is so unbelievable that if it weren't so frightening it would be laughable. In fact, I don't think you'll believe it.'

I glanced at my watch. It would be another twenty minutes before we arrived at our destination. 'Then perhaps you should tell me about it,' I said.

She leaned back, her gaze fixed on nothing in particular. 'It began seven days ago. I was staying at a small hotel in

Denver. That particular morning, while I was having breakfast, the waiter brought over a large bunch of red roses, two dozen of them. There was a note with them addressed to me although I'd no idea who could have sent them.

'The note said that I would receive a bunch of red roses every morning — but there would be one less each day. Then there'd be a day when I'd get the final, single rose. On that day I would die.'

'Not a very nice romantic note to be sent by anyone,' I remarked soberly. 'You say you've no idea who could have sent them?'

She shook her head. 'Naturally I inquired at all the florists I could find in Denver. None of them had received such an order. And certainly none had ever been delivered to the hotel.'

'And did any of the staff at the hotel know anything about them?'

She shook her head emphatically. 'I made discreet inquiries. All they could tell me was that they had been found at the reception desk but nobody had seen who'd put them there.'

'That's very strange. And you've received others every day since including this morning?'

'Yes. There were seventeen this morning.' She dabbed at her eyes with her handkerchief. 'I don't know if it's someone who really means to kill me — or some crazy person who wants to frighten me. Believe me, if that's their intention, they're certainly succeeding.'

'Can you think of anyone who would want to do something like this?'

She shook her head again. 'No one.'

I didn't tell her it was the kind of stunt the Organization sometimes pulled. That would have really scared her and I knew I'd get nothing rational out of her if she became hysterical.

'What do you think is happening, Mister Merak?' Her voice was just above a whisper, barely audible over the pounding clatter of the train wheels. 'If anyone means to kill me, why use this bizarre method of warning me when it's going to happen? I don't understand it at all.'

'My guess is that someone is deliberately trying to drive you crazy, although I

8

must admit it's a very odd way of doing it,' I suggested. 'In either case I think you need help — professional help.'

'Someone like you, Mister Merak?'

'Hey now, lady, hold on a minute. I'm not touting for business. I've only just finished one hard case. I'm not looking for any more at the moment.'

'I've got a little money of my own. I can pay you. Besides, I believe you're a man who can keep this to himself. If it has anything to do with the other side of the family, they won't be too pleased if they knew I'd engaged a private detective. But I've got to do something or I will go crazy.' She was pleading now but those little mice were running around inside my head. They were telling me that there was a lot more to this case than I'd learned so far. If, for some reason, the Mobs were involved in this, the last thing I wanted was to be mixed up with them.

It also seemed far too much of a coincidence that she had picked me to sit beside and pour out this fantastic story. Those little mice were suggesting that she'd deliberately chosen that particular seat and had known who I was before she spoke. Certainly what she had told me was intriguing. Indeed it was so intriguing that I made up my mind almost at once.

'All right, I'll take your case Miss Somerville. Where are you staying in L.A.?'

'At the moment I'm with my mother at the Ocean View hotel. It's on the seafront. You can't miss it.' She rummaged inside her handbag and brought out a card with her name and the address on it. 'Just ask for me when you come. The receptionist there knows me very well. In fact, she's the only one at the hotel I can really trust.'

'You're not staying at home?'

She hesitated and then said in a low voice, 'We had to sell the house when my father died. There were a lot of debts and — '

'And your relatives refused to help you?'

'The quarrel between my father and uncle was very acrimonious. I don't know much about it but after my father died they cut us off completely, never even acknowledged our existence.'

'I get the picture. I'll see you about this time tomorrow,' I told her, taking the card and slipping it into my pocket. 'For the time being, I shouldn't worry too much. This seems like a very nasty joke someone is playing on you.'

Glancing through the window I saw that the storm had moved away inland and we were pulling into the depot. She shook hands with me as we parted on the platform and the last I saw of her she was standing at the top of the stairs, her right hand lifted in farewell.

There seemed no point in going back to the office at that hour. I'd left Dawn Grahame, my assistant, in charge when I'd left three days before for Denver. As there'd been no word from her, I reckoned business had been slack without any major problems. I decided to find some nice, cosy bar where I could get a drink and something to eat before going back to my apartment for the night.

I found this small place only a block away from the train depot and went inside. There was a vacant table at the far

11

side and I sat down and ordered a steak — well done. It came ten minutes later together with a cup of hot, black coffee. I ate ravenously, realizing I hadn't eaten a real meal since early that morning. I had just pushed the empty plate away and ordered another coffee when this guy walks up to the table and sits down in the seat opposite me.

Leaning back in my chair I gave him the once-over. I'd never seen him before but I recognized the type. Snappy dresser, thin black moustache, hair slicked back so that it shone in the light. I figured him for an attorney of some kind.

'You're Johnny Merak.' It was more of a statement than a question so I guessed he already knew who I was.

'So?' I said.

'You were on the train that arrived twenty minutes ago from Denver.'

I experienced a momentary surprise but did my best not to show it. 'Tell me something I don't know.'

He leaned forward, placing his elbows on the table. 'You've been talking to someone and that could land you in big trouble. I suggest you forget all about the woman you met on the train. Unfortunately, she's — how shall I put it? — mentally unstable. I had hoped that someone would have been available to accompany her on the journey. In the past she's approached other passengers and made a nuisance of herself with wild stories that have no basis in fact.'

'You're trying to tell me she's insane?'

'That isn't the precise term I'd use. I think paranoid would be a better word. She believes that someone is out to kill her. If she annoyed you with any of her nonsense I apologize on behalf of the family and trust you'll forget all about it.'

'Well, thank you for telling me all of this,' I said. 'I must confess I was a little worried about her but now you've explained everything I guess that the only thing for her is some kind of psychiatric help.'

'And I can assure you we intend to see that she gets it.'

'We?'

'The family, of course. I'm merely their lawyer.' He brought a card from his pocket and gave it to me, pausing to see if I had anything further to say. When I hadn't he turned and left. Outside, he stood for a moment on the sidewalk and then a dark blue limousine pulled up beside him. He got in and it drove away.

Taking out a cigarette, I lit it and drew deeply on it. Things were moving pretty fast now and I guessed the Somervilles were at the back of it all. From all that my visitor had just told me there was only one thing I was really sure of. Edith Somerville was as sane as I was!

★ ★ ★

The next morning the early traffic was worse than usual and it was almost nine-thirty when I finally got to the office. Dawn was already there when I arrived. She walked up to me, placed her arms around my neck and kissed me. 'I missed you, Johnny,' she said huskily, 'even though it was only three days.'

'Now that's what I like to hear first thing in the morning,' I told her.

'Anything dramatic happened while I've been away?'

She shook her head. 'Nothing at all,' she said, going back to her desk and switching on the electric kettle. 'How did things go in Denver? Did you sort out your client to his satisfaction?'

'Everything went fine in Denver,' I replied. 'It was on the way back yesterday when the strangest thing happened.'

She made the coffee and brought it over, sitting on the edge of my desk. 'Want to tell me all about it?'

I nodded. 'Since it may be another case for you I reckon you should know all about it.' In between sipping my coffee, I told her what had happened on the train. She listened attentively, not interrupting once. When I'd finished, she looked thoughtful and then said, 'Do you honestly think she was telling the truth, that someone is out to kill her and ticking off the days by sending her a bunch of roses every morning? It's all too fantastic to be true.'

I shook my head. 'No, Dawn. On the

contrary, it's all too fantastic not to be true.'

'And this man you met last night. It sounds as though he was warning you off taking her case, telling you that you'd better not accept her as a client.'

'That's possible, of course. If that was his intention these people have certainly wasted no time getting to me.'

She arched her eyebrows. 'Then you believe it all?'

'Somehow, I do. The first thing I'd like you to do, Dawn, is get as much information as you can on the Somerville family. See if you can dig up any dirt there might be in their past and especially on this quarrel she said happened between her father and her uncle. It was about three years ago.'

She went back to her chair. 'What are you going to do?'

I thought for a moment. 'I reckon I should have another talk with Edith Somerville. She may have calmed down a little by now. I'm damned sure there's a lot she didn't tell me yesterday.'

Dawn left ten minutes later, taking her

notebook with her. I finished my cigarette and then went down into the street to where the old Merc was waiting. I was on the point of getting in when a car drove up and parked right behind me. It was a police car. A familiar figure got out and walked towards me. Lieutenant Shaun O'Leary. His attitude told me this wasn't a social call. He was there on business and it evidently concerned me.

'Glad I caught up with you before you left, Merak,' he said brusquely. 'I just need to ask you a few questions. It won't take more than a couple of minutes of your very valuable time.'

'Go ahead Lieutenant. If I can help the LAPD in any way I'm always glad to do so.'

'I understand you've been away for a few days.'

"That's right, Lieutenant. Don't tell me you've missed me.'

He ignored the sarcasm but his eyes narrowed down a little and I guessed he wasn't in the mood for any wisecracks.

He took out a notebook and consulted it, flipping over the pages, running his tongue around his lips. 'You sat beside a middle-aged woman for most of the journey — Edith Somerville. Is that correct?'

I felt a sudden stab of surprise. 'Yes. Don't tell me you've got cops following me whenever I go?'

'Not you, Merak. I can pick you up any time I feel like it.'

'Hold it there, Lieutenant. You're telling me you had someone tailing Edith Somerville? But what the hell has she got to do with the police? She's not a wanted criminal, is she?'

'According to her uncle, Herbert Somerville she's being treated by some top psychiatrist and it seems this guy believes that if anyone like you starts poking into her life it could make things much worse for her.'

'So someone in the family has got to you, Lieutenant. They want you to put the squeeze on me. Is that it?'

'If you want to put it that way, Merak — the answer is yes. I don't know who did this. All I know is that the order came from very high up in the department.

Drop this case, Merak.'

'And if I don't?'

O'Leary's face took on a nasty look. 'I'm sure you don't want to lose your license.'

I grinned. 'Now come on, Lieutenant. You know very well my license was issued by the state — and not the police department. And whether you believe it or not in my estimation Edith Somerville is just as sane as you and me. If necessary, I'll go into a court of law and swear to it.'

The Lieutenant scratched his chin. 'Why the hell are you so damned keen to take this case, Merak? Is it because you now know somebody big is out to stop you and you're hoping to get a bit of publicity out of it? Or is it because you think you're always right and you've just got to prove it?'

'It's nothing like that,' I told him as I moved towards my car. 'I've got a really nasty feeling up here,' I tapped the side of my head.

'About Edith Somerville?'

'That's right. I'm convinced someone is out to kill her and they're trying to drive her crazy before it happens.'

'Are you serious?'

'I'm perfectly serious, Lieutenant. I spoke with her for almost an hour yesterday on the train. I'm absolutely sure her life is in great danger. That's why I don't intend to drop the case.'

O'Leary looked as though he had a lot more he wanted to say. Instead, he merely shrugged and went back to his car, got in, and slammed the door shut. I waited until he'd gone before getting behind the wheel of the Merc and driving down to the promenade.

I soon picked out the Ocean View Hotel. It stood a little way back from the promenade and although not as grand as some of the others in the neighbourhood it had a homely look to it. I could understand why Edith Somerville and her mother would choose it as a place to stay.

I parked the car a short distance away, got out, and walked up to the entrance. The guy on the door looked to be well into his sixties and he'd probably had better positions than the one he now occupied. Some of his past showed through in his attitude as he saw me.

He eyed me up and down as if I were something that had just been washed up by the tide. 'Did you wish to see someone resident at the hotel, sir?' His tone implied that if I were looking for a room, I should try elsewhere.

I nodded. 'I believe a very good friend of mine is staying here,' I told him. 'Edith Somerville. Perhaps you'd be good enough to tell her I'd like to see her.'

His face changed a little at the mention of her name. Perhaps he was wondering how I could possibly know anyone in the Somerville family. Or maybe he'd noticed the tell tale bulge where the .38 nestled just beneath my left arm and figured I might be a cop.

'Who shall I say wishes to see her?' he asked frostily.

I gave him my card. He studied it minutely before turning and going inside. He was gone for five minutes. 'I'm afraid that Miss Somerville is not in at the moment, sir,' he said. He sounded pleased that my journey had been for nothing but then he added, 'However,

Mrs. Somerville is in and has asked to speak to you. If you'll follow me.'

I followed him. Inside the hotel, I was handed over to a young woman in a neat blue uniform. Evidently she was the receptionist Edith had mentioned because, unlike the guy on the door, she seemed to have a liking for private detectives.

'Do you happen to know where Miss Somerville has gone?' I asked.

She shook her head. 'All I know is that she seemed upset by something that happened while she was having breakfast.'

'Let me guess. She received a bunch of red roses — sixteen of them.'

She looked at me as if I was Sherlock Holmes and Hercule Poirot rolled into one. 'Why yes. How on earth did you know that?'

I grinned. 'Let's just say that I'm psychic. Tell me, did you see who delivered those roses?'

She hesitated for a moment, then shook her head. 'I've been behind the desk for most of the morning. But a little while ago I was called away to the manager's office. I wasn't gone for more than ten minutes. They were on the desk when I came back.'

'And they weren't there when you left ten minutes earlier?'

'That's right.'

Without saying anything more, she led me into a large room where several of the residents were seated, most of them reading newspapers. Crossing to the far side, she approached the old woman sitting a little away from the others.

She was probably in her early seventies, silver haired, bearing a striking resemblance to her daughter. She motioned me to the empty chair beside her. The receptionist hesitated and then drifted away like fog.

'I understand you wish to see my daughter, Mister Mcrak,' she said. 'May I ask why a private investigator should be interested in her?'

'I presume you're aware of this charade about the roses.' I watched her closely as I spoke, noticed the abrupt tightening of the lips and how some of the colour drained away from her cheeks.

'So she's already told you about that?'

'She has — yesterday when we met on the train.'

'Do you believe there's anything really sinister behind it?'

'I'm afraid I do. I don't want to frighten you but I believe someone is out to kill her and has chosen this rather bizarre method to drive her insane before she's killed.'

'I see.' She sank back into her chair and this time her face was totally drained of colour. 'Can you help her? I'm afraid she's never been the same since her father's death three years ago. She took it very badly.'

'She asked me for help yesterday and naturally I'll do everything I can to find out who this person is behind all of this. But it isn't going to be easy. She can't think of anyone who'd want to kill her. Can you, Mrs Somerville?'

She thought for a moment and then shook her head. 'I'm afraid not.'

'I see.' I could tell right away that she was lying but I didn't know why. 'Then do you know where she is now? The receptionist told me she left after breakfast immediately she received those roses.'

'She may be on the beach somewhere. She sometimes goes there particularly when she wants to be alone.'

'Thanks.' I got up. Her eyes followed me as I left.

There were quite a lot of folk about at that time of the morning, mostly tourists. Vigilant lifeguards sat in the shade watching the surfers out on the ocean. I looked along the beach in both directions but there was no obvious sign of Edith Somerville. I walked along a bit and then I spotted her sitting on a small bench. As I'd guessed, she was alone staring at nothing in particular.

I walked over and sat down beside her. She jumped and looked momentarily startled. Then she recognized me.

'Why, Mister Merak. I didn't expect to find you here. Are you following me?'

'Not really,' I replied. 'But I told you yesterday that I'd call in to see you.'

She bit her lower lip. 'I'm sorry. Of

course you did. I'm afraid I'd completely forgotten.'

'You received another bunch of roses this morning.'

'Yes. It's quite clear that, whoever it is, they've followed me here.' There were tears in her eyes and she took out a dainty lace handkerchief and dabbed at her eyes.

I sat back, hoping to put her at her ease. 'Is there any more you can tell me? I spoke to your mother a little while ago. I asked her if she knew of anyone who might want you dead. She said she didn't but I've been in this business long enough to know when people are lying to me.'

Her head jerked up sharply and there was a curious expression on her face that I couldn't analyze. 'You believe she knows something I don't?'

'It's possible. I'm not sure whether she's trying to protect you or there's something more to it. Whatever it is, I can't help you unless everyone is frank and open with me. There's something about this case that seems to be giving everyone the jitters. I've already been warned off it twice.'

She looked puzzled. 'I'm afraid I don't understand. Someone has told you not to take my case?'

'That's right. Last night some guy interrupted my meal to tell me that your family didn't want any private investigator delving into their business and your doctor had advised that if I didn't back off your illness would become even worse.'

'My illness?' Her surprise was genuine. 'I don't know why anyone should say that. There's nothing wrong with me. Who else has tried to warn you off?'

'Lieutenant O'Leary of the LAPD. It seems that some word came from high up ordering me to drop the case.'

'I see.' She squared her shoulders in a defiant gesture. 'So what are you going to do? Can they do anything to you if you refuse? The last thing I want is for you to get into trouble with the police on my account.'

'There's nothing they can really do except make it more difficult to get hold of any information. I've a few contacts in the police department but I've no doubt they'll be told to tell me nothing.'

'So there's really very little you can do?' she said dismally.

'Don't worry. Even without their help there's a lot I can do.'

She wiped her eyes again. 'But if that first note meant what it said, I've only got a little over a fortnight to live. Someone is going to kill me and I don't know who or why.'

'Just stick with it and leave everything to me,' I told her. I tried to force a little confidence into my voice but it wasn't easy. This case seemed to have more twists and turns than a maze.

I got up. 'There'll be a lead somewhere.'

I walked away, leaving her gazing out at the ocean, an expression of pure misery on her face. I was feeling a little that way myself although I'd never have admitted that to her. The truth was I had no leads at all. My only hope now was that Dawn had managed to come up with something.

I got back to where I'd left my car near the hotel, opened the door, and slid behind the wheel. Putting the key into the ignition I was about to turn it when a voice behind me said, 'Don't start the car, Johnny. I want a word with you and here is as good a place as any to have it.'

'Harry!' Somehow I got the name out. This was the last person I'd expected to see. Harry Grenville was an FBI agent based in New York and I'd worked closely with him in the past. It had been Grenville who'd put me onto the straight and narrow after I'd managed to get out of the Mob.

'What brings you to L.A.?'

'The same case you're now working on. That meeting you had with Edith Somerville on the train yesterday was no coincidence. She came to us nearly a fortnight ago asking for our help. Seems that, even then, she was afraid someone was out to kill her.

'My boss was of the opinion that she was just another screwball who sees enemy agents and killers behind every tree. I don't see it that way and somehow I convinced him there might be something to her story and suggested that you ought to look into it so I gave her your description and told her you'd be on the train yesterday.'

'But why me, Harry?'

'Because you know the Organization inside out. You know its methods and how it hides its information.'

'The Organization!' I turned to stare at him. This was something as expected as Christmas Day in May. 'You think the Mobs have a hand in this?'

'I'm damned sure of it. Not that I can convince my boss of that. Furthermore, the Somervilles are a pretty important family in L.A. Plenty of connections with Washington. Any hint that they may be connected with any of the outfits could have serious repercussions.'

'I can believe it. So you want me to stay with the case but not a word about what you've just told me?'

'That's right. But be careful. If anyone inside the Organization should suspect that you know about this I wouldn't give much hope for you seeing your next birthday. If you find anything you can get me at this number.' He handed me a card with a number written on it.

Opening the door, he got out. I watched him walk to his car parked on the other side of the promenade. Little bits of the puzzle were now beginning to fall into place but they were forming a picture I didn't like.

The fact that the Mobs seemed to be involved added a new and more deadly dimension to the case.

Dawn was back at the office when I got there ten minutes later. She looked pleased with herself and I guessed she'd had a successful hour at the Library. Taking off her coat, she asked, 'Did you manage to get any more out of Edith Somerville?'

I sat down. 'Not much,' I admitted. 'As I'd expected, she got sixteen red roses at breakfast this morning.'

'So whoever is behind all of this has got pretty close tabs on her.' Dawn pursed her lips.

'Too damned close. They seem to know exactly where she is every minute of the day. But that's the good news.'

Dawn looked startled. 'You mean there's worse?'

'I'm afraid so. I'd just got downstairs this morning when O'Leary drove up. Somehow, word had come down from high up to tell me to drop this case right away. He even threatened to have my license revoked. Then when I got back from having a talk with her there was someone waiting in the back of my car — an old friend of ours.'

'Who?' She seemed to be dreading the answer.

'Harry Grenville.'

'Harry? What did he want?'

'It seems that the Feds are also interested in Edith Somerville. Harry wants me to stick with the case. His boss doesn't accept it at the moment, but Harry's certain the Somerville's are closely connected to the Mobs.'

'Do you think that's why O'Leary warned you off the case?'

'Could be. But from what O'Leary said it seems someone with plenty of muscle has got on to someone high up in the LAPD, and warned them off. Not only the police, but I've been warned off too. My guess is there's something really big going on and they want it kept hidden. And the Somervilles have enough muscle to make things very difficult for anyone who starts nosing around. But what did you find out?'

'Plenty.' She flipped open her notebook. 'When old Henry Somerville founded the banking chain in L.A. a couple of centuries ago it seems everything was above board. There was no hint of any scandal or mishandling of funds. I couldn't find much about the period when his only son Charles was in charge. It wasn't until after he died that certain rumours started to be spread around.'

'That would be when his two sons took over the business,' I interrupted.

She nodded. 'Exactly. Herbert, the older brother had the major share and he made all of the decisions where the business was concerned.'

'Did you discover anything about this quarrel that seems to have divided this family?'

She shook her head. 'I couldn't find anything about that but it seems to have been an acrimonious affair whatever it was.'

I got up. 'Then I reckon it's important to find out what it was and I think I know where I can get some of that information.'

2

Revelations From The Past

Once behind the wheel of the Merc I drove across town to Mancini's bar. I knew this was Sergeant Kolowinski's day off and exactly where he'd be. As a bachelor he divided his time between the precinct and Mancini's. Sometimes I wondered if he ever slept at all.

Someday, his superiors would find out about his drinking habits and start asking questions. I only hoped it would be after he retired and got his pension and not before. Even at that time of the morning, Mancini's was open. I often wondered whether they ever closed at all.

Jack Kolowinski was there in his usual place holding up the bar. I slid onto the stool beside him. He didn't look round but he knew who it was. There was a half-empty glass in front of him. For a couple of minutes he sat there, simply staring straight in front of him.

Then he said gruffly, 'What is it you want this time, Johnny?'

'Surely a guy can come in and have a drink with an old friend without wanting anything, Jack,' I said.

'I can't remember any time when you didn't want some information.'

'All right. I need your help.' I signalled to the barkeep to bring a couple of drinks and waited until they came before saying, 'I want you to think back about three years, Jack. You probably remember a guy called George Somerville. His death made headline news.'

'Somerville?' He turned the name over in his mind. 'The name's familiar, but — '

'It was believed he committed suicide by throwing himself off the top storey of the Marsden Hotel.'

When he hesitated, I went on, 'You should remember everything, Jack. You were one of the investigating officers.'

He rubbed his chin. It made a tiny scratching sound in the silence. 'Do you know how many people jump out of top storey windows every year in L.A., Johnny?'

'Quite a lot I suppose. But Somerville was a member of the big banking family. His death made quite a story for the newspapers.'

He tossed down half of his drink. 'All right, Johnny. I remember it well. There was some kind of meeting in the penthouse suite that evening. What it was about we don't know because no one ever talked about it. Seems that, sometime during the evening, this George Somerville complained about not feeling well and he left to room to get some air. We got that much, according to the witnesses. Not long after that he was found on the sidewalk directly below one of the top windows. He'd fallen more than three hundred feet onto the sidewalk.'

'And from what I can gather, there was an inquest and the verdict was suicide.'

'That was the verdict,' he agreed. 'But several of us on the investigating team didn't agree with it. To me, it was murder. There was no doubt in my mind that someone heaved him out of that window.'

I took a sip of my drink. 'Why do you say that, Jack? Do you have any evidence to substantiate it?'

He shrugged. 'I went up to that room about five minutes after we arrived at the scene. That would be less than half an hour after it happened. The ledge of that window was about five feet from the floor. I've seen plenty of suicides where folk have jumped and in every case they've climbed out over the ledge and they nearly always hit the ground feet first. I also saw the body and Somerville had hit the sidewalk head first. I'll stake my pension he was helped on his way down.'

'I see.' I noticed his glass was empty and ordered another. He was still fairly sober. I didn't want him too drunk. Once he started talking to me from floor level he would be no use to me.

'Was there any evidence of that apart from what you've just told me?'

He thought for a moment; then nodded, 'There was something. The carpet just in front of the window. There were marks as if there'd been some kind of a scuffle and I also noticed a small tear in the material but I couldn't say how recently it had been made. Then there were the plane tickets.'

'Plane tickets?'

'That's right. We found two tickets in his pocket. According to his wife he'd planned a holiday for the two of them to Acapulco two days after all this happened. Now you tell me, Johnny — does a guy arrange what was probably a second honeymoon and then take a dive a couple of days before setting off?'

'Surely that would go a long way towards proving it was murder,' I said.

'It was never bought up at the inquest. The coroner ruled it was irrelevant to the case. A few of us at the precinct tried to get this evidence put to the D.A. but orders came from somewhere upstairs that the case was closed. No further investigation was to be carried out.'

'Then obviously somebody really high up gave that order.'

'Sure.' He paused; then looked directly at me. 'You're not thinking of reopening the investigation, are you, Johnny? If you are, you'll get no help from O'Leary or anyone in the police department. And the records all mysteriously disappeared some time ago.'

'Now why doesn't that surprise me?' I finished my drink and left him still staring at nothing in particular. I doubt if he even knew I'd gone.

I went back to the office. Dawn glanced up as I sat down behind my desk. She must have noticed the expression on my face for she said, 'How much did you find out, Johnny? Anything important?'

'I had a word with Jack Kolowinski. What he told me changes everything. It seems there's plenty of evidence to show that George Somerville's death was neither suicide nor accidental.'

'You mean he was murdered?'

'Not only that — but everything was hushed up at the inquest. I'd say that Edith had figured this out for herself and it was this that affected her and gave the family an excuse to have her put in the care of some psychiatrist.' I lit a cigarette as she brought over a mug of hot, strong coffee. 'You know, a lot of things are beginning to add up.'

She looked puzzled. 'What kind of things?'

'Somebody wanted Edith's father dead — but why? It was obviously someone who had a big pull with the D.A. and the police department.'

'One of the Big Boys in the Organization, perhaps?' she suggested

I sipped the coffee slowly. It burned the back of my throat but I was hoping it would allow me to think more clearly. What she said was certainly possible. Men like Sam Rizzio, and Shaun Malloy who'd taken over the other big outfit following his uncle's death, both had the muscle to make sure that George Somerville's death was put down to suicide.

I finished my coffee and at that moment the phone shrilled loudly. Picking it up I said, 'Merak.'

It was Lieutenant O'Leary on the other end of the line and he didn't sound too pleased. 'I want you over at the Ocean View Hotel right away, Merak.'

'Why — has something happened to Edith Somerville?' Why she should jump into my mind I didn't know and I wasn't going to find out for he just said, 'Get here now.'

'I'm on my way, Lieutenant.' I put the phone down and stubbed out my cigarette.

In response to Dawn's inquiring look, I said, 'It's O'Leary. He wants me at the Ocean View Hotel pronto.'

'Did he say why?'

I shook my head. 'No. I guess he's a guy who likes surprising people.'

*　*　*

A quarter of an hour later I pulled up in front of the hotel and pushed my way past the guy standing at the door. He made to say something but then he must have remembered me from when I'd been there earlier.

O'Leary was standing impatiently in the foyer when I entered. 'You took your time,' he snapped.

'Have you seen the traffic out there, Lieutenant?' I replied, ignoring the sarcasm in his tone.

'All right. Just come with me.' He led the way towards the stairs.

I followed him to the top floor, wondering what was coming next. We entered a short corridor and I noticed a uniformed cop standing outside one of the doors. Opening the door, he motioned me inside. It was a bedroom and there was someone lying on the bed. The covers and pillows were all disarranged, evident signs of a struggle.

For a moment I was sure it was Edith Somerville lying there. It wasn't. It was Mrs. Somerville. Her eyes were wide open, staring up at the ceiling but not seeing it. I looked across the bed at O'Leary.

'One of the maids found her like this an hour ago when she brought up her usual breakfast,' he explained. 'According to the doctor she's been smothered.'

'And her daughter?' I asked. 'Has she been told?'

'The doctor is with her at the moment. She's taken it pretty badly and it may be some time before we can get a statement from her.'

'Clearly the victim put up a struggle before she died.' I looked around the room and then at the door. 'Have you checked if there was a forced entry?'

'There are no obvious signs but we'll make a thorough check.'

I walked over to the door and bent to examine the lock. Peering closely at it I noticed the minute scratches in the metal and called O'Leary over. Bending forward he soon verified them for himself.

'So this lock has obviously been picked.' He got up. 'That means it could be anyone in the hotel — or even a stranger.'

'It could,' I agreed. 'So we still have no definite leads as to her killer.' I changed the subject. 'Do you mind if I question Edith Somerville? She might find it easier to talk to me than the police.'

He turned that over in his mind. I expected him to object — but he didn't.

'OK. Go ahead. But if she has anything important to say, you tell me right away.'

'I'll do that, Lieutenant.'

I found Edith downstairs in the lounge. There was a guy with her and I guessed he was the doctor. The receptionist was standing in the background looking as though she hadn't yet taken in what had happened. I guessed it wasn't every day anything like this happened in the hotel.

I pulled up a chair from one of the tables, spun it round, and sat down, resting my elbows on the back. Edith was dabbing her eyes with a dainty silk handkerchief. She recognized me at once.

'Mister Merak. I suppose you know what's happened?'

I nodded. 'I've just left Lieutenant O'Leary upstairs. I'm really sorry about your mother but if we're to find her killer I'm afraid there are some questions I have to ask.'

'I've just given Miss Somerville a sedative,' interrupted the doctor. He gave me a funny look. 'Are you someone connected with the police?'

'Not exactly,' I told him. 'I'm a private investigator. Miss Somerville hired me a few days ago and I thought she might prefer to talk to me before the police start grilling her.'

He glanced at Edith who merely

nodded her head in confirmation. 'Very well but don't make it too long. I think you can see what her mental state is at the moment.'

'I'll try to make it as brief as possible.' Looking across at her, I asked, 'Do you know if your mother had any enemies, anyone who would want to do this?'

She bit her lower lip in concentration before saying, 'I can't think of anyone who would want to kill her.'

I paused for a moment before asking her the next question. 'Could it have been anyone connected with either your father or your uncle?'

I noticed the abrupt change of expression that flashed across her face but it was gone in an instant. 'Why should you think that?' Her voice shook a little and I knew my question had momentarily taken her completely off guard.

'Your father died some three years ago and I'm aware that it was put down to suicide. Now, however, there seems to be a lot of evidence that points to him being murdered.'

For a moment I thought she was going

to faint but she somehow pulled herself together. 'I don't believe that for one minute,' she said harshly. 'I was there when it happened. He left the meeting because he didn't feel well and needed a breath of fresh air. There was no one with him when he left the room.'

I made to say something more but the doctor interrupted me. 'I think that's enough for now. I want her to get some sleep.'

I got up. 'I'm sorry if I upset you, Miss Somerville,' I said. 'Believe me, I'm only trying to get to the truth.'

Back on the top floor I found O'Leary deep in conversation with Kolowinski. They broke off as I approached.

'Did you get anything out of her?' O'Leary asked sharply.

'Not much I'm afraid. The doctor had given her something to make her sleep but there was something I noticed.'

'Oh, what was that?'

'I told her it was my belief that her father had been murdered three years ago. In my job, Lieutenant, you get to be pretty good at reading what people are thinking and I'm quite sure she believes it was murder too.'

O'Leary looked as if he were going to choke. 'You told her you think her father was murdered? The inquest stated it was suicide. Why the hell did you tell her that?'

'Let's just say I wanted to provoke a shock reaction. Also, after hearing a lot of evidence that was never brought out at the official inquest, I'm also damned sure George Somerville was killed. He certainly never took his own life. Someone helped him over that window ledge and gravity did the rest.'

O'Leary's eyes narrowed at that. 'I'm giving you fair warning, Merak, leave George Somerville out of this. That case is closed — and it stays closed. You can go now unless you've any more crazy suggestions to make.'

I shrugged. 'Not right now, Lieutenant. But I am going to reopen that case and see what I can find.' I turned and left. I could feel his gaze boring into my back as I walked away.

I'd just stepped through the front

entrance of the hotel and was walking towards my car when I suddenly realized I was not alone. Two guys had appeared from nowhere and were walking one on each side of me. They each grabbed one of my arms and hustled me forward along the gravel drive.

'Hey!' I said. 'Just what *is* this?'

'Don't make any trouble, Merak,' grunted one of them. 'Someone wants to see you and he doesn't like to be kept waiting.'

I guessed at once. There was only one man in the whole of L.A. who sent for people in this manner. The Big Boss, Enrico Manzelli!

There was a large black limousine waiting at the end of the drive. One of the guys opened the rear door and thrust me inside, sliding in to sit beside me. The other got into the front passenger seat and said something in low tones to the driver.

I knew better than to protest. With men like these you did exactly as you were told.

That way you stood a better chance of

coming back alive. The drive out to the mansion where Manzelli lived took the best part of twenty minutes. Most of the way we were travelling at something in excess of eighty but although we passed a few speed cops no one made a move to pull us over.

Manzelli's cars were known all over the city and the cops evidently had better things to do than interfere with whatever Manzelli was doing. Some rookie cop might overstep the mark and try to issue a speeding ticket — but he only did it once.

In daylight, Manzelli's place looked even more secluded than at night when I'd last visited it. I reckoned there wasn't another place within a ten-mile radius. As usual, I was taken around to the rear entrance. The Big Boss was seldom seen beyond these walls but his influence extended over the whole of the city. Nothing went on without him knowing about it. The bosses of the various outfits received their orders from him and all of them knew better than to disobey them.

One of the two guys took off while the other, still keeping a tight grip on my arm, hustled me along a wide corridor to the door at the end. Thrusting the door open, he led me inside and, without a word, pointed towards the chair in front of the huge mahogany desk.

I sat down and waited. The door behind me closed softly and I knew I was alone. I sat there for at least five minutes and all the time there was the feel of eyes watching me, scrutinizing every movement I made. It wasn't a nice feeling.

Then a faint whisper of sound reached me, and a door behind the table slid open. There was a faint light visible momentarily in the doorway. A moment later, however, it was blotted out entirely by the enormous bulk of the man who came in. Pulling back the chair opposite me, Manzelli lowered himself into it.

'I apologize for the manner in which you were brought here.' His voice was strangely soft for his size. 'But unfortunately some of those I ask to come and see me prove to be extremely uncooperative.'

I'll bet they are, I thought. A lot of those who came here never left again

— at least not on their own two feet.

I said nothing, waiting for him to speak first. He had something on his mind otherwise I wouldn't be there but for the life of me I couldn't figure out what it could be.

Finally, he leaned forward, a difficult manoeuvre because of his huge bulk, and placed the tips of his fingers together. I was beginning to feel uncomfortable under his piercing scrutiny.

'I had you brought here because of certain events which both puzzle, and disturb me. I'm aware of the meeting you've had with this woman, Edith Somerville. I presume you've already reached the conclusion that this was not a purely accidental meeting. Nor was it due to coincidence.'

'That possibility had occurred to me,' I admitted.

He nodded. 'There is something here that disturbs me greatly. But first I want to speak about the other player in this strange drama.'

I looked up sharply at that. 'The other player?' I repeated. 'Who might that be?'

'Her uncle, Herbert Somerville. I gather that he owns one of the largest banks in Los Angeles. A very influential man by all accounts.'

'That's true,' I said, wondering what interest Manzelli had in him.

Manzelli stared at me and I could feel his gaze rubbing at the back of my skull. 'I've received certain information, which I'm inclined to believe is true, that this man Somerville has been engaged in talks with someone high up in the Organization. As to the nature of these talks I unfortunately have no information and that is something I want you to find out.

'It is possible that Somerville wants a stake in some of our business. However, as you're undoubtedly aware from the time you spent in the Organization, no outsider can be allowed to become a part of any of the outfits. I need to know Somerville's intentions as soon as possible and also who he's talking to.'

He paused for a few moments and then went on, 'I presume you are willing to do this little thing for me.'

'Of course.' I knew that poking my

nose into the activities of the various outfits would be both difficult and highly dangerous — but no one said no to Manzelli if he wanted to remain healthy.

'Good. You've proved to be extremely useful in the past, Merak. I do not forget such things.' He slid his left hand under the table. I guessed there was a button there for the next moment the door opened and one of the guys who'd brought me there came in.

'Our guest is ready to leave.' Manzelli said. 'I look forward to receiving the information I need in the very near future. Goodbye Mister Merak.'

'I'll do my best,' I said.

The big guy led me outside to where the limousine stood waiting. Getting in I sat back to admire the scenery. I always felt a little better whenever I left Manzelli's. The guys who ran the outfits you could sometimes talk them out of doing anything that might shorten your life — but not Manzelli. Like God, he held the power of life and death in his hand.

The driver dropped me off at the

Ocean View Hotel. There was no sign of O'Leary's car there so I guessed he'd finished his questioning and gone back to the precinct. The Merc was still there, however. I got behind the wheel and drove slowly back to the office.

Dawn was out but she came in ten minutes later with some sandwiches and four cans of coke. 'I thought you'd be back,' she said, taking our lunch from the large brown paper bag, 'so I brought enough for two.'

'Thanks.'

'What did the Lieutenant want?' she asked. 'Has something else happened?'

'There's been another murder,' I told her.

Her delicate eyebrows lifted in sudden surprise. 'Edith Somerville?'

Shaking my head, I said, 'Wrong guess, Dawn. It was her mother. She'd been smothered.'

Dawn stared at me. 'This case gets screwier every day. Why would anyone want to kill that old woman?'

'That is something I have to find out, and quickly.'

'You? But surely this is a homicide case. It's up to O'Leary to find the killer.'

'I'm afraid not, Dawn. I'd just left the hotel to come back here when I got a summons from Manzelli. It appears he's worried that Herbert Somerville is getting a little too cosy with someone in the Mobs. I have to find out who it is and what's behind it all.'

She threw her hands wide in an exasperated motion. 'Johnny, you're not in the Organization now. You don't have to do what Manzelli says every time he needs someone to stick their neck out and put their lives on the line.'

'I only wish it were as easy as that. I'll bet more than half of the high-flying politicians in the city are wishing the same thing.'

'So what do you mean to do now?'

'I reckon I'll put together a list of possible suspects and see if any can be eliminated. I still have this feeling that Edith Somerville isn't telling me everything.'

When the time came to close up the office for the evening, I had got nowhere.

There was a lot of circumstantial evidence pointing at people who might want either George Somerville or his wife dead but nothing that would stand up before a grand jury.

As I locked the door, Dawn asked, 'Are you coming up to my place tonight, Johnny?'

'I'd sure like to,' I told her, 'but I think I'll take a walk. I need to clear my head and there's someone I want to have a word with.'

'Would you like me to come with you?'

'I think this is something I have to do on my own. I'll see you tomorrow morning.'

She looked disappointed as she went along to her car but she said nothing more.

I watched her drive away and then got into the Merc and drove down to the Strip. The casinos were just beginning to fill with the night time customers. The guy I was looking for ran one of them. Venito Carini had been a small-time crook working for one of the smaller outfits when Sam Rizzio had taken him under his wing. Now he was something of a big shot in the Mobs.

I went in and gave the place the once-over. It was filling up quickly with most of the tables already occupied. I'd only taken a dozen steps, however, when there was a bruiser standing beside me.

'What are you doing here, Merak?' he grunted. 'If you've come to make trouble you can leave right away.'

'Now why should I want to make trouble?' I asked innocently. 'I just want a word with Venito.'

'Who?' He tried to look as if he'd never heard the name.

'All right,' I said. 'I understand you don't have much of a memory. Both of us know he's the boss here. Perhaps if I were to tell you I'm working for Enrico Manzelli your memory might come back.'

My mention of Manzelli's name brought about a miraculous change in him. If his face had gone any whiter it would have shone in the dark.

'You'd better come with me.' He led the way across the room to a door in the far wall and knocked softly on it.

Someone called something from inside and opening the door he said, 'I've got that private investigator Merak here, boss. He says he's working with Manzelli.'

A moment later, Carini was at the door. The smile on his face might have been painted on. 'Come in, Johnny.' He motioned me inside. 'It isn't often we see you in this part of town.'

He closed the door and motioned me to a chair. Sitting down opposite me he lit a cigarette with fingers that shook a little. Leaning forward, he offered one to me. He was a little guy with a narrow chin and close-set eyes giving the outward appearance of a ferret. 'What's the word from Manzelli?'

I sat back. 'Nothing to do with you directly,' I told him, noticing the instant look of relief that crossed his face. 'I'm working on a case for him, one that directly involves a guy called Somerville — Herbert Somerville. Perhaps you've heard of him?'

He thought for a minute, looking down at the glowing tip of his cigarette; then shook his head. 'The name means nothing to me, I'm afraid,' he replied finally.

'He's head of one of the biggest banks in L.A,' I said, hoping to jog his memory.

His expression changed at that. 'A banker. I figured you were talking about some member of the Organization. Now you come to mention it, I have heard his name before.'

'Do you remember where?' I asked.

He pursed his lips, looking even more like a ferret. 'There's a rumour that he's well in with Shaun Malloy though I doubt if you'll find anyone who'll confirm it. Malloy plays his cards close to his chest.'

'I know what you mean,' I said, stubbing out my cigarette. 'I don't suppose he ever comes into any of these places along the Strip.'

Carini shook his head. 'He may like a gamble at the tables. A lot of these really wealthy guys do but since most of these are controlled by Rizzio it isn't likely.'

His remark prompted another question in my mind. 'You're quite well in with Sam Rizzio. If Malloy were to offer him several million bucks for these gambling joints do you reckon he'd take it?'

Carini didn't hesitate. 'Not a chance. You know how things are between Rizzio and Malloy. They hate each other like poison.'

'I guess you're right. It was just an idea I had.' I scraped back my chair and got up. 'Thanks for the information, Venito.'

'Any time, Johnny. But you didn't hear any of this from me.'

'Not a word of it.'

I went out onto the sidewalk. It was getting dark now and the ocean was a mass of deep purple, stretching all the way to the horizon. Walking down onto the beach I suddenly realized I was hungry. It was several hours since I'd had anything substantial to eat. I looked around and soon spotted this hotdog stall. He was serving a young couple and looked as if he were closing up for the night.

Going over, I waited until he'd served the customers in front of me. Looking up, he said, 'What'll it be, mister? A hotdog or a burger?'

'Give me a hotdog,' I said. 'No, make it

two. It's a long time since I've eaten.'

I watched as he stabbed the weenies with his fork, placed them between the rolls and squeezed a liberal portion of mustard along them.

Glancing up, he said, 'Would your friend like one as well?'

Turning my head slightly, I saw the big guy who stood directly at my back. The sand had undoubtedly deadened the sound of his approach and I knew there was a gun pointed straight at my spine.

Swallowing hard, I said, 'Sure, make one up for him. He's paying.'

'Don't get funny with me, Merak,' grated the guy at my back. 'Someone wants to have a word with you and he doesn't like to be kept waiting. Now move!'

'Hey!' The stall owner had just woke up to the fact that this was a heist. 'What's going on?'

'Just stay out of this,' grunted my companion. The muzzle of the gun was grinding into my back now as he pushed me away from the stall.

'All right,' I muttered. 'I'm coming. I'd

like to eat this hotdog on the way, if you've no objection. I've had nothing to eat since breakfast.'

'You're still trying to be funny,' growled my companion. 'If the boss wasn't so anxious to talk to you, it'd give me the greatest pleasure to put a slug into your back.'

'Sure you would. That's the only way guys like you can think.'

We walked back along the beach towards the promenade. There was a large limousine waiting against the sidewalk. None of the lights were on. Two anonymous shadows were visible in the front.

3

The Big Fix

The rear door popped open and my companion thrust me inside, crushing in beside me. Then he leaned sideways, slid his hand inside my jacket and took out the .38 from its holster.

The man sitting in the front passenger seat turned his head. In the darkness, I could make out very little of his features but he was someone I didn't recognize.

'You've been extremely foolish, Merak,' he said in a soft, cultured tone. 'You've been warned to drop this case you've taken on for my niece and now I believe you've been asking around about me. Why is it that men like you can't accept the fact that your services aren't required and leave things at that?'

I sat back. So this was Herbert Somerville. Something didn't add up here. I didn't believe in coincidences, only in cause and effect. To me, that could only mean that Carini had got on the phone to this guy even before I'd stepped out of the casino. Although he was not one of the mob bosses that didn't make my position any less precarious.

'In my business I have to ask a lot of questions about a lot of people,' I said.

'And sometimes that can be dangerous. I assure you that I do not advocate violence but there are times when it becomes necessary. If I were to ask you to drop this investigation into my family's affairs, and make it worth your while to do so, I somehow think you'd refuse.'

'You think right,' I said. 'I've never taken a case and accepted money, and then gone back on it. The fact that you're scared of what I might dig up means you've got a lot to hide.'

After a pause, he went on, 'I have nothing to hide, Mister Merak, but I do intend to protect Edith. Her mental condition is now extremely unstable and any further probing on your part might just push her over the edge.'

I knew he was lying. He wanted me off

his back just to save his own neck. Whatever deals he was making with the Mobs, my guess was it was highly illegal. Probably he wanted a part in some of the action and if that ever came out, he'd lose everything. It had to be something really big for him to take that risk.

Leaning sideways he said to the driver, 'I think it's time we got this over.'

Twisting the key in the ignition, the other started the engine. We drove forward along the promenade. I expected them to take me to some secluded spot well away from town where there would be no witnesses to my eventual demise. Instead, the car stopped after travelling only a couple of hundred yards.

The big guy next to me opened the door and got out. Grabbing me by the arm he hauled me after him. Somerville was already outside the car.

I took a swift look around me. We had stopped at the very end of the road. To my right was a wide circular area where vehicles might swing round and return along the route they'd come. On my right was a steep rocky slope down towards the beach and beyond that, just visible, was the ocean.

Somerville came right up to me while the punk held my arms tightly behind my back. Before I guessed what was coming, Somerville swung his right fist. It hit me on the temple, jerking my head back. I sucked in a deep breath and waited for the next blow.

As I tried to focus my eyes I saw Somerville walk back towards the car. He signalled to the hood sitting behind the wheel and I heard him say, 'Give him the once-over and then see to it that he doesn't bother me again.'

The guy came at me quickly, a leering grin on his swarthy features. I knew he was enjoying this. His fist smashed into my stomach, knocking all of the wind from my lungs. Another hammer blow came at the base of my spine so that I went down onto my knees.

There was no way I could protect myself. By the time they'd finished I was on my hands and knees. Blood dripped into my eyes making it almost impossible to see anything. These guys were professionals. They knew exactly where to hit to cause the most pain.

How long the battering went on it was impossible for me to tell. Everything around me was nothing more than a red blur of agony.

Then, dimly, I heard Somerville say, 'That's enough. Get rid of him. We don't want anyone nosing around and finding him.'

One of the guys placed his foot under my right side and kicked me solidly in the ribs. A second later, I went over the edge of the rocks. I went rolling down the steep slope, my arms and legs hitting outcrops of rock as I fell. Then my head struck an out-jutting boulder and a merciful blackness surrounded me, washing away the pain.

I must have been unconscious for some time. Feeling came back into my body and with it the agony. With an effort, I managed to lift my head and force my vision to focus on my surroundings. There was a dull booming in my ears and for some reason my legs were icily cold and wet. Then details slowly swam into sharp focus.

I was lying on wet sand at the base of the slope and already the surf was washing over my lower body. My left hand was resting on something hard that moved beneath my fingers. It was my .38. Evidently those hoods had tossed it down after me. The grim thought came to me that they'd done it so that I had the chance to shoot myself in the head before the Pacific engulfed me completely. Gritting my teeth as pain spasmed through my shoulder, I thrust it into its holster.

Pressing my back against the rocks, I somehow got my legs under me and straightened up. One look behind me was enough to tell me I didn't have an icicle's chance in hell of scaling the slope and the tide was coming in fast. Even though it hurt my chest, I drew in several deep breaths in an attempt to force my brain to think clearly and coherently.

It was then I realized there was a confused noise sounding above the booming of the surf. A full minute passed before I recognized what it was. Someone was shouting down to me from the top of the slope. Even then it took a while for me to make sense out of the words.

'Hang on, Merak. We'll soon have you out of there.'

I hung on. Then a few moments later something rattled down the slope beside me. It was a long rope.

My hands were numb with the cold. There was scarcely any feeling in them but somehow I managed to get it secured around my waist. Then I was being hauled up the steep incline. Sharp rocks cut into my back and legs but I didn't mind. By some miracle I was getting out of there. Three minutes later I was sitting on the grass at the top and someone was bending over me. There were lights shining from a couple of cars and I noticed the other end of the rope had been tied around the rear bumper of one of them.

'Thanks.' I managed to mumble the word.

'Another ten or fifteen minutes and you'd have been a goner, Merak. How the hell do you always manage to get yourself into trouble?'

I experienced a sudden sense of shock. It was O'Leary's voice. Screwing up my eyes I noticed Sergeant Kolowinski standing a few feet away.

'I seem to have upset some people and they decided they didn't want me around any longer,' I said. 'But how the hell did you find me?'

'A call came through to the precinct from a concerned citizen. He said he had a hotdog stall on the sand and he'd witnessed what he thought was an abduction at gunpoint. He'd heard your name mentioned and seen you forced into a car that drove off in this direction.'

'Thank God for the honest citizens of L.A.,' I said fervently. 'Where would we be without them?'

'You'd be dead,' O'Leary said. 'By the look of you I reckon we'd better get you to a hospital right away. You're a mess. Do you have any idea who did this to you?'

For a moment, I considered lying but then thought better of it. 'Sure I know who it was, Lieutenant. It was Herbert Somerville.'

'Somerville?' There was a note of genuine astonishment in his voice. 'Why the hell should he want to beat you up and then leave it for the ocean to finish you?'

'I think I can guess. He's got something to hide and he thinks I'm getting just a little too close to finding out what it is. His excuse, however, is that he's afraid his niece will go completely insane if I continue with her case.'

Changing the subject I said, 'There's no need for the hospital, Lieutenant. I've been worse, If you'd just take me back to where I left my car I'll — '

O'Leary shook his head. 'If I let you drive in that state, Merak, you'd be a danger, not only to others but to yourself. If you're set against going to the hospital I'll have you taken to your place and you can pick up your car tomorrow.'

I knew there was no point in arguing with him. I owed him my life so I figured I'd better do as he said.

Kolowinski drove me back to my

apartment. He didn't say much on the way. No doubt he was wondering why Somerville had such a grudge against me that he wanted me killed. But he wasn't an inquisitive kind of guy. Not like Lieutenant O'Leary.

'Thanks for the lift, Jack,' I said as I got out.

'You're sure you'll be all right?' There was genuine concern in his voice.

'Sure, Jack, I'll be fine.' I closed the car door and waited until he'd gone, then went inside my apartment, switching on the electric fire. Then I poured myself a stiff drink and sat sipping it, feeling the warmth soaking into my numb body.

Turning events over in my mind, I wondered if Carini had told anyone else about my visit. Those little mice inside my head were telling me that if he had I could be in even deeper trouble. Not only Somerville but one or two other guys might try to put a permanent end to my career. I told myself that that was something I had to find out and the sooner the better.

Finishing my drink, I reached a sudden

decision. It was probably the most stupid decision I'd ever made in my life. I'd been beaten up, thrown down onto the beach, knocked unconscious and left to drown, only to escape the Grim Reaper by the skin of my teeth. Anyone who had an ounce of sanity would have gone to bed and slept through until morning. Me — I decided to go and have it out with Carini at that very moment.

Perhaps the going-over I'd received at the hands of Somerville's bruisers had affected my reasoning but two minutes later I was outside the door and walking towards the promenade. There were few pedestrians around at that time of the morning otherwise I might have been picked up as a vagrant.

I knew Carini wouldn't be asleep. His type remained wide-awake so long as the punters were in the casino and the money was rolling in. The problem would be getting him alone without any of his henchmen around.

The lights were still on all along the Strip and now I came across more of the night people. Several gave me funny looks as I made my way through them. No doubt most of them figured I'd been in some kind of accident and was trying to find my way home.

I stood outside the joint where I could see most of the people inside. For a while there was no sign of Carini. Then I spotted him near one of the roulette tables talking to one of the guys who worked there. They seemed to be having an argument of some kind. Whatever had happened between them, he suddenly grabbed the guy's arm and began hustling him towards the entrance.

Almost without thinking I stepped to one side, into the shadows, my right hand inside my jacket. They stopped within three feet of where I was standing. Thrusting the guy out onto the sidewalk, Carini hissed, 'Get the hell out of here. If I see you here again you're a dead man.'

The guy went off and before Carini could turn to go back inside I stepped forward and rammed the .38 hard into his ribs. 'Make a sound or move I don't like, Carini,' I said softly, 'and it'll be you who are the dead man.'

I felt him stiffen. He didn't turn but I knew he'd recognized my voice. Swallowing hard, he said, 'What the hell do you want now, Merak? I told you everything I know a little while ago.'

'I think we'll go somewhere where we can talk again without any of your hired killers around. Now move and don't try anything funny or it'll be the last thing you do.'

'You wouldn't dare shoot me in front of all these people.' He tried to force a note of confidence into his voice and failed miserably.

'No? I wouldn't stake your life on it. And I've got Manzelli to back me. I reckon if I were to let him know what happened tonight you'll find yourself knocking on the Pearly Gates before you knew what hit you.'

I guess he knew I meant every word I said for he moved away from the casino entrance and walked slowly beside me until we came upon a narrow alley filled with trash. A few moments later we were away from the crowd on the boulevard.

'What the hell is all this about, Johnny?'

'It's about you and me having a talk together and less than ten minutes later I'm picked up by one of Somerville's hired killers and taken to him. I just hope you're not going to claim it must have been a coincidence because I don't believe in them. Someone phoned Somerville the minute I left this casino and informed him that I'd been in asking questions about him.'

'Now hold on a minute, Johnny. I never passed word to him about you being in the casino.'

I shook my head and pushed a little harder with the gun. 'Sorry, Venito, but I don't believe you. My guess is that you've been in with this guy Somerville for some time. You knew that Manzelli has asked me to look into this case so Somerville must have some hold over you or you'd have thought twice about going against Manzelli's orders.'

He pressed his lips tightly together and remained silent.

'Come on, Venito, you'd better talk or they'll find you here in the morning and then you won't be able to do any talking.'

He was sweating now. I could see his face shining in the dimness. Lifting the .38 I pressed it hard against his forehead.

Licking his lips, he said hoarsely, 'All right. All Right. I'll talk. There's a rumour that Somerville is trying to get a piece of Malloy's action in return for a hell of a lot of dough. They've been having meetings for some time. I don't know what it is that Somerville wants exactly but he's somehow got the idea that you're investigating him. All of us along the front have been told to let him know if you come around asking questions. We either do it, or we're finished.'

I lowered the gun slowly. I reckoned he was telling the truth. 'All right, Carini,' I said. 'Go back to your crooked games but don't try to mess with me again.'

He turned to leave and then made a dive for his pocket with his left hand. I'd guessed he'd try something like that. Before he could pull out the weapon there my own gun connected with the back of his skull and he dropped without a sound. I left him there and stepped out into the street. He'd wake up sometime with a sore head but I doubted if he'd try anything like this again.

The casino was still proceeding as normally. No one seemed to have come looking for Carini. Maybe they'd thought he'd slipped out for a drink or a breath of fresh air. I walked along to where I'd left the Merc earlier in the evening. It was still sitting there waiting for me.

I got behind the wheel and turned the key in the ignition. Like the warm-hearted creature it was, it started immediately and I drove back to my apartment. The streets were almost empty of traffic at that time. A couple of late-night cabs passed me looking for fares.

Once inside my place I locked the door and then went into the bathroom and doused my face with cold water, wiping off the blood. It was now a little after two and I figured I might get a few hours sleep before going into the office. Swallowing down a couple of painkillers I slid between the sheets and switched off the light.

When I woke the next morning the sun

was glaring through the window and my watch told me it was a little after eight. I'd managed to sleep for six solid hours and although my head and ribs still hurt, I felt able to meet whatever the day might bring.

There was no one at the office when I got there but Dawn came in five minutes later, took one look at my face, and came over to the desk.

'What happened to you?' she asked, concern written all over her face. 'You look as if someone's been using you as a punchbag.'

'You're not far wrong,' I told her. 'I ran into Herbert Somerville last night with a couple of his boys. I guess they didn't like the look of my face and decided to alter it.'

'I'll make you a coffee and then you're going to tell me all about it.'

She listened in silence as I went over the details of the previous night. Her expression didn't change until I came to the bit where O'Leary had arrived on the scene and almost certainly saved me from becoming fish bait.

'So he now knows that Somerville is definitely into something with the Mobs?'

'I guess so. But it isn't O'Leary who worries me — it's Carini. Somerville has got some hold over him which is why Carini phoned him immediately after I left the casino.'

'I think you're in this mess too deeply to be able to get out. Frankly I can't see what your next move is. I know you've got Manzelli behind you but that won't stop a bullet if these other hoodlums don't take any notice of what Manzelli says.'

Before I could say anything further there was the sound of footsteps in the corridor outside. A moment later there came a knock on the door.

'The door's open. Come in,' I called loudly.

It opened and Edith Somerville stood there. She looked as if the best thing for her would be a good night's sleep. There were dark circles under her eyes and she looked as if she'd been crying. I got up and took her arm, leading her to the chair.

'Would you like a drink?' I asked.

She threw a quick glance in Dawn's direction and then said, 'I'd like something stronger than coffee if you've got it.'

Opening the drawer in my desk I took out the bottle of whiskey and poured her a liberal measure into the glass. She picked it up with hands that were shaking visibly, holding it in both hands.

After taking several sips, she put the glass down and said in a faint whisper, 'I'm still getting those damned roses every morning, Mister Merak.' Lifting her head she looked directly at me. 'Are you any nearer to finding whoever is sending them?'

'I'm afraid not,' I admitted. 'It probably isn't any consolation to you but my own feeling is that this is some kind of hoax. Killers don't usually tip off their victims.'

'You think someone is doing this just to frighten me. If that's their plan, it's certainly succeeding.'

'There is one other possibility,' I told her. 'It may be that someone is trying to drive you insane and have you committed to an asylum.'

'But who would want to do anything like that?'

'Someone who has something to gain by putting you away where you can't manage your own affairs,' Dawn interposed.

'And if we're right,' I said, 'that person would be your uncle. With your mother now dead, he's your only living relative. Do you stand to inherit anything from your mother?'

She hesitated at that. I knew it was something she didn't want to talk about but if I was to get to the bottom of this case it was something I had to know. Finally she nodded. 'My mother has left me quite a substantial sum but to suggest that my uncle is behind all of this is absurd. He's extremely wealthy, far more than I'll ever be. I can't see him wanting any of what I have.'

I lit another cigarette. We seemed to be getting nowhere, just running around in circles. I noticed her glass was empty and I poured out another drink. She drank it down almost at once, grimacing a little as the raw liquor hit the back of her throat.

Then she got up and stood for a moment looking down at me. There was something at the back of her eyes that I couldn't analyze. Anger, disappointment, fear? It was impossible to tell. Before going to the door, she said, 'I'm making the arrangements for my mother's funeral. A lot will depend upon when the police will let her body go but I'll let you know what it is as soon as everything is arranged. I'd like you to come, both of you.'

'We'll be there,' I promised.

4

Rizzio Pays A Call

It was mid-morning the next day when things started hotting up. At the moment I had very few real leads. Sure, I knew that Somerville was trying to buy his way into one of the Mobs but that was about all. I was no closer to finding this killer than I had been at the beginning.

Dawn hadn't arrived yet and while I was waiting for her I went over every one who might be a suspect. I felt sure there was something I'd overlooked, something important. But those little mice were lying dormant at the moment and no help to me at all.

I picked out the sounds of high heels in the corridor outside. The door opened and Dawn stood there but she wasn't alone. There were three guys with her and one of them held what was obviously a gun in her back. With a savage push the guy forced her inside. My other two visitors came in and I recognized one of them right away. Sam Rizzio!

He walked forward and sat down in the chair opposite me. There was a look on his face that told me this was no social call. He was here for trouble — big trouble.

'Take out that gun you're carrying, Merak, and put it on the desk where I can see it. Otherwise your girl friend might get a slug in her back and I'm sure you wouldn't want that to happen.'

I did as he said. Those little mice had woken up as I tried to figure out why Rizzio was here and what he wanted.

'I suppose you know why I'm here, Merak,' he said softly.

'I'm sorry, Sam,' I said. 'But at the moment I've no idea what you're talking about.'

'Then you've got a very short memory. I suppose you're going to tell me you didn't go for a late-night walk down to the Strip. And don't give me the old excuse that you suffer from insomnia.'

So that was it. I wasn't certain whether

he was talking about Somerville or Carini but I knew I'd soon find out. I leaned back and tried to speak casually. 'So I had an argument with Herbert Somerville and he left me to go down with the tide. But what's that to you?'

His eyebrows went up a shade. 'Somerville is nothing to me. I'm talking about Carini. When one of my boys gets threatened I have to take care of it. I'm sure you understand. In a way I like you, Merak. You've been very helpful to me in the past but now you're questioning some of my best men, making threats against them if they don't give you the answers you want. That makes you a very dangerous man where I'm concerned as head of this outfit. Much as I dislike it, I'm afraid I'll have to have you removed, permanently. I also regret that your lady friend here will have to go too. Like you, she knows too much for her own good. Before the boys take you both for a little ride what did you think you'd get out of Carini?'

'All I wanted was information but for some reason he decided to let this guy

Somerville know everything. My guess is the two of them are working together. So how did you know it was me at the casino last night?'

'As far as I was concerned there's only one guy in L.A. dumb enough to try to pull a stunt like that, especially after you'd already been warned off. So you wanted information . . . What kind of information?'

'Since you've already made up your mind to kill us I guess there's no reason you shouldn't know. Someone, and I'm damned sure it's Herbert Somerville is trying to buy his way into the Organization.' I knew Dawn was watching me closely. 'But it isn't just me who wants this information. Manzelli is in on this too and I guess he won't be too pleased if anything prevents me from going ahead with this investigation.'

His expression sharpened at that. He wasn't sure whether to believe me or not. Depending upon whether he believed Manzelli was backing me or not would decide whether or not he would kill the both of us. I decided to push on while I had the initiative.

'Someone high up in the Organization is trying to bring in an outsider — Herbert Somerville, the banker. You know the rules as well as I do. The Bosses make all the decisions and no outsiders are to have a say in these.'

He seemed suddenly interested. Pulling out the chair in front of him, he sat down, resting his elbows on the desk. 'And what's your interest in this, Merak?' he demanded. 'Knowing your reputation you're figuring on making something out of it. What is it — publicity or money?'

I began to breathe a little more easily. He seemed to have temporarily forgotten his threat to kill both of us and I wanted to keep it that way.

'Would you believe me if I told you that Manzelli is getting a little worried?'

His answer was blunt and to the point. 'No, I wouldn't.'

'Then I reckon you should get in touch with him before you do anything stupid. I guess you already know what happened to Joe Malloy.' Joe had been the top man in a rival outfit and had been killed in a car crash just after trying to put Manzelli out of business. Only Manzelli and I knew it was no accident. He'd tried to push Manzelli from his position as top man and had paid the price.

It was now a case of me threatening Rizzio and he didn't like that, especially not in front of two of his own men. But Rizzio was no fool. Whenever Manzelli gave an order, everyone jumped from the top politician to the little guy on the street. No one got to be where Rizzio was without taking every little detail into consideration. And he knew I'd never have dared to talk to him like this unless I did have Manzelli's backing.

He sat silent for several moments drumming with his fingers on the desk. I could almost hear the little cogwheels inside his brain grinding away in his head. This wasn't the way he had intended this meeting to go and he wasn't sure what to do now. I lit a cigarette and waited for him to make up his mind.

Finally, he said, 'If you are working for Manzelli I figure we have to work together. You reckon that whoever's trying to worm his way into the Organization is also responsible for these killings? I hear there's been another one at the Ocean View. Is that true?'

'You hear quite a lot, Sam. It only happened a little while ago . . . But it's time enough.' I drew deeply on the cigarette. It was strange, the change that had suddenly come over Rizzio. He'd been quite prepared to eliminate Dawn and myself when he'd come into the office. Now he was on the point of cooperating with me. I could think of only one reason for this abrupt change in attitude. He wasn't the one working hand in hand with Somerville but he sure as hell wanted to know who it was. Not only that, but these killings could be bad for business and the one guy who might be able to discover who was behind them was Johnny Merak.

'Who was the victim?' he asked after a long pause.

'Mrs. Somerville. Herbert Somerville's sister-in-law.'

'It seems to me that these Somervilles are right in the middle of all this.' He gave me a shrewd look. 'So where exactly do you fit into all this?'

I wondered whether to tell him everything from my first meeting with Edith Somerville on the train. Then I figured — what the hell? I'd sooner have him on my side in spite of how O'Leary and Harry Grenville might feel about it. Not only that, but with his connections it would not take him long to find out just who was cosying up to Herbert Somerville.

He listened while I gave him the full story, occasionally nodding and at other times tapping the desk top with his fingers. When I'd finished he leaned back and took a golden cigarette case from his vest pocket. Taking one out, he offered one to me. I took that as a good sign. Sam Rizzio wouldn't waste even a cigarette on someone he meant to get rid of.

Lighting up, he spoke through the cloud of smoke. 'Very well, Merak, let's get down to business. Your real concern is finding out who's threatening to kill Edith Somerville and somehow you've linked this to her father's death three years ago.'

'That's right.'

'And you want me to discover which of the outfits is trying to cut Herbert Somerville in with the Organization?'

'That's it in a nutshell,' I said.

Turning his head slightly, he addressed the two bruisers standing near the door. 'Have either of you picked up anything about this?'

Both men shook their heads in unison like Tweedledum and Tweedledee.

Looking back at me, he went on, 'I reckon I can vouch for all of my own men, Merak. Anything like this I'd have heard about.'

'So it has to be one of the other outfits.'

'I'll ask around.' He stubbed out his cigarette and got up. 'If I do find anything I'll let you know. In the meantime, take my advice and watch your back.'

Once he'd gone, taking his two henchmen with him, I let out a long sigh. I could see that Dawn was still shaking slightly but trying not to show it.

'That was a close thing,' I said finally. Opening the drawer of the desk I took out the bottle of Scotch and two glasses. 'I think you could do with a drink too, Dawn,' I said, half filling a glass and handing it to her. For once she made no objection but took it and sipped it slowly. Pouring a generous measure into my glass I downed half of it in a single swallow.

'He really would have killed us if you hadn't mentioned Manzelli, wouldn't he?'

I nodded. 'I doubt if he'd have thought twice about it. But however much he tries not to show it, he's like the others — scared of Manzelli.'

Eyeing me over the rim of her glass, Dawn said soberly. 'Just one thing, Johnny. Don't get the idea that you're invincible just because you have Manzelli at your back.'

'I won't,' I promised.

'There seem to be quite a lot of people out there who'd like to see you dead. It only needs one of them who couldn't give a damn about Manzelli and you're finished.'

She turned quickly back to her desk but I could have sworn there were tears in her eyes. I knew she'd never turn round and show them so I placed my hands on her shoulders and said soberly, 'That reminds me. I want you to find out when Mrs. Somerville is going to be buried. I reckon we should attend the funeral.'

On her last visit Edith had promised to tell us when it would be but so far there'd been no word from her.

'Why are you so anxious to go, Johnny? I know Edith asked us to attend but you hardly knew the woman.'

'That's true. But there's an old belief that the murderer is always present at his victim's funeral and I want to be there just to see who attends — and who doesn't.'

'I'll check with her and go with you.' Dawn nodded. 'Two pair of eyes are better than one.'

The funeral was held five days later.

★ ★ ★

It was a cold, still afternoon with fog that had earlier rolled in from the sea. It soaked through our clothing until, after only a few minutes, we were both chilled to the bone. The tall elms around the perimeter of the churchyard were ghostly shapes seen intermittently through the swirling wraiths of white. Dawn and I had picked a spot a short distance from where the grave had been dug. Now we waited.

There were quite a lot of people already there. Some I recognized but the majority were strangers. The line of cars arrived five minutes later, moving with an almost military precision through the open gates. The first one came to a stop almost immediately in front of us. I saw Edith Somerville get out. She was accompanied by a tall, well-built man. Not until he turned in our direction did I recognize him. Herbert Somerville! That started me thinking. Was it possible that this death had brought about some kind of reconciliation between the two sides of the family? I wondered. I wouldn't have thought it possible after all that had happened but I had to believe the evidence of my own eyes.

Dawn had noticed too for she said in a low voice, 'Isn't that Edith Somerville and her uncle?'

'The very same,' I replied.

She pursed her lips for a moment before going on, 'They seem to be on quite good terms at the moment.'

'You're right. I wonder what's brought that about.'

I watched them closely for a few moments and then switched my attention to the others who had now alighted from the cars and were congregated around the grave.

The thick blanket of fog now made it difficult to make out their faces. Most of them I didn't know but there were one or two I did recognize — top men from most of the outfits.

Outwardly they were just businessmen. You'd see them at any fund-raising parties for poor children giving generously of their ill-gotten gains. In reality they were nothing more than vicious killers.

Some distance away, standing inconspicuously among the headstones, I spotted O'Leary and Sergeant Kolowinski. Perhaps the Lieutenant held the same theory as I did. Somewhere among this assembly was the killer we were after. It was a sobering thought.

The minister finished his monotonous address, closed the prayer book, and stepped back. Very slowly, the coffin was lowered into the ground. Edith came forward and I noticed Herbert held her arm tightly as she took a handful of earth from the box and scattered it over the coffin. Once he had done the same he led her back.

Those little mice inside my head were telling me that this didn't make any sense. From everything I'd been told, those two were bitter enemies. Now they seemed to be the best of friends. I wondered if Lieutenant O'Leary had made the same observation and what he'd make of it.

The minister hurried through the service. No doubt he was feeling as cold as we were. Once the ceremony was over I took Dawn's arm and ushered her to where Edith was standing. Herbert was a short distance away talking to one of the Mob members I'd earlier recognized.

'Mister Merak,' she said as I approached. She held out her hand. 'It was good of you to come. I didn't expect to see you.' She glanced at Dawn.

'To be quite honest, I didn't expect to be here myself.' I turned to Dawn. 'This is my assistant, Dawn Grahame,' I said, introducing them. 'You met her in my office the other day. She helps me with most of my cases and does her best to keep me out of trouble.'

'I'm pleased to meet you, Miss Grahame.' Edith shook hands with her. 'Doubtless Mister Merak has told you about me.' She looked directly at me. 'As you've probably guessed there were nine roses waiting for me this morning.' She seemed close to tears as she added, 'Isn't it strange to have the remaining days of your life measured by the number of flowers you receive each morning?'

She took a small handkerchief from her pocket and dabbed at her eyes.

'I see you've made up with your uncle,' I inclined my head in Herbert's direction. 'From what you've told me I never thought that would happen.'

'What's the use of prolonging a quarrel about which I really know so little?' After a brief pause, she continued, 'I've been meaning to call at your office again to see if you've made any progress but with all that's happened — ' She broke off helplessly.

At that moment, Herbert spotted me. He came storming over, his face twisted into a scowl of anger and utter astonishment. 'What the hell are you doing here, Merak?' he hissed in a low voice.

'I reckoned you'd be surprised to see me after our last little talk.'

He grabbed me by the arm and pulled me away from the others. I could guess at the thoughts running through his mind. I was the last person he expected to see and he was trying desperately to figure out what had gone wrong with his plan to get rid of me.

He bared his teeth keeping his voice down so that only I could hear it. 'By rights you should be — '

'At the bottom of the Pacific.' I finished his sentence for him. 'The trouble with me, Somerville, is that I keep popping up when I'm not expected. The trouble for you is that O'Leary happens to be around right now and I don't see any of your hitmen with you.'

'I don't know how the hell you got away, Merak. But you've already been warned to stay away from my niece. I've already told you what her mental state is like. If you persist in having any further contact with her I'll see you dead and this time there'll be no mistakes.'

He spun on his heel and stormed off towards the waiting car.

Edith was still standing where I'd left her, next to Dawn. She gave me an inquiring look. 'What did my uncle want with you, Mister Merak?' she asked. 'I've never seen him so angry.'

Shrugging, I replied, 'We had a little disagreement about how your case should be handled. He's not pleased with the way I'm going about it. I have the feeling he wants me to drop it.'

A stubborn expression came over her face. 'But you're not going to do that, are you?'

'I'll stick with it for as long as you want me to,' I promised.

'I have to admit that Herbert never wanted you to take the case and as for me, I'm becoming more and more scared every day. Unfortunately, you don't seem to be any nearer to finding this man who means to kill me than when you first started.'

She turned back towards where Herbert was waiting beside the car. Over her shoulder, she said softly, 'Please help me if you can. You're the only hope I have and there are only — ' She hesitated and for a moment seemed on the verge of tears before adding — 'nine days left.'

'Believe me, I'll do everything possible,' I said. I tried to sound reassuring but deep down inside there was this hollow feeling that nothing I could do would prevent this mysterious killer from striking again.

5

Deadly revelations

There was something important lurking at the back of my mind when I woke the next morning. Whatever it was, it refused to go away but it never crystallized into anything definite so that I could recognize what it was that was bothering me.

Dawn was already up and there was the smell of coffee coming from the direction of the kitchen. I dressed quickly and went through. Dawn put down a heaped plate of bacon and eggs and sat down opposite me.

'You look as though you've got something on your mind, Johnny,' she said.

I nodded. She had this knack of reading my innermost thoughts. Sometimes, it scared me. 'There's something nagging away at the back of my mind but I'm darned if I know what it is.'

'Maybe it was something that happened yesterday at the funeral,' she suggested.

I mentally ran through all that had happened the previous day but still nothing emerged. Finally, I muttered, 'It'll come back to me sometime. Right now there's work to do.'

Dawn arched her brows. 'Such as?'

I pushed the empty plate away and sipped the hot coffee. 'I'm sure now that Sam Rizzio isn't in with Herbert Somerville. So that leaves us with the other outfits. It's possible that one of the smaller gangs is the culprit but somehow I don't think so. Herbert Somerville is too big and important a man to go for anything but the biggest. If it isn't Rizzio, my guess is this has to be Malloy's.'

'So what do you know about them?' Dawn asked.

I lit a cigarette. 'From what I've managed to pick up through the grapevine, that outfit is now being run by Shaun Malloy, Joe's nephew.'

'Do you know anything about him?'

'Not very much,' I admitted. 'You'll

find his name in the file.' I pointed towards the nearby cabinet.

Dawn got up and opened the second drawer, riffling through the files until she found the one on Shaun Malloy. She opened it and spread it out on her desk. There was only one page and she ran her gaze swiftly down it.

Finally, she said, 'As you say, Johnny, there isn't much. He came over here from Ireland at the age of fifteen and spent several years in Detroit and Chicago before moving to L.A. and joining his uncle. Picked up by the cops twice and charged with first-degree murder, possession of an unlicensed firearm and possession of heroin. It seems he got off on all three charges due to lack of evidence. Some of the members of the outfit didn't like the idea of him taking control. Two of them were found shot in some warehouse two days later.'

'No doubt anyone else who disagreed decided they'd better fall into line,' I remarked dryly. 'Evidently he intends following in the family tradition. He's not going to be an easy man to approach.'

'And if he is on more than friendly terms with Somerville it's not likely he's going to tell you anything,' Dawn retorted.

I turned that over in my mind. There was one way that you usually got people to talk and that was if they were looking into the wrong end of a gun. But I didn't want to voice this to Dawn. I knew it was something she'd definitely not want me to go through with. But at the moment it seemed the only way.

'I think I'll have to have a word with Malloy. It may be the only way to get some answers.'

'That would be completely stupid. He'll shoot you down the moment he gets sight of you.'

'Probably not if I were to phone him first. The only way you get to see the Big Boys is if they come to you or you make an appointment. That way they may be inclined to listen.'

'And then they'll have you killed. Don't forget you were responsible for what happened to his uncle.'

'Maybe he'll reckon I did him a favour.

After all, he's the boss now.'

Dawn shook her head in a gesture of resignation as I lifted the phone and dialled Malloy's number. Some guy answered.

I asked to speak to Shaun Malloy.

There was a pause and then the guy said, 'Who is this?'

'The name's Merak,' I told him.

There followed another pause, longer this time. I figured the other might be asking Malloy if he wanted to see me. But he wasn't because he came on again and said, 'Mister Malloy isn't here. I suggest you ring again in a few days. Right now, he's at the summer house.' There was a click and the line went dead.

'Well?' Dawn asked as I put the receiver down. 'What did he say?'

'I didn't get to speak to him. It seems he's out at his summer place. I guess I'll have to go there and there's no time like the present.'

'You'll not have a chance. That place will be crawling with hoods.'

'Perhaps. But I'll get no answers just

sitting here.' I got up and reached for my hat.

'All right, if you're so damned stubborn. But this time I'm coming with you.'

One look at her face told me it would be useless to argue with her. 'You know what'll happen if anything should go wrong.'

She nodded. Walking to my desk, she opened the top drawer and took out the Luger. 'I told you the night we first met that these men don't scare me.'

'All right. But stick with me whatever happens. And if you have to use that gun, don't hesitate.'

We went down to where the Merc was standing beside the sidewalk. A quarter of an hour later we left the suburbs behind and were on the coast road heading east. Here was where the rich and the famous lived during the summer, away from the dust and heat of the city. On one side was the Pacific, a vast expanse of blue with the white surf pounding the beaches. Several surfers were out riding the crests of the rollers. On the other side were the fancy beach houses.

Malloy's place was well separated from any of the others. Evidently, like his uncle, he preferred the solitude. I parked the car some distance from it and took out the binoculars from under the dashboard. Leaning on the wheel I focussed them on the white building and examined it closely. There seemed to be no sign of life although the curtains and two of the lower windows were open.

'That's strange,' I said after a few moments.

'What is?' Dawn asked.

I handed her the binoculars. 'There doesn't seem to be anyone about. I'd have expected someone to be outside on the patio on a day like this.'

'Maybe they're all out surfing,' Dawn suggested.

'That's possible. But I've got a funny feeling about this. That looks like Malloy's car at the side so he's here all right.'

Dawn lowered the binoculars and rubbed her eyes. 'Unless they've spotted us and are in there preparing a welcome party for us.'

I looked along the beach in both directions. There were few people about. One or two were splashing around in the sea some five hundred yards away but for the most part the place appeared deserted.

Opening the door I got out. 'Stay right here, Dawn. I'm going to take a look around. Something here gives me a funny feeling in my stomach.'

Taking out the .38 I walked toward the front of the house, expecting to hear a shot at any moment and feel the impact of a slug. But there was nothing. The utter silence remained unbroken.

Half a dozen steps led up from the beach to the door. I took them two at a time and pressed myself hard against the wall beside the door. If this was a trap I was going to have to walk right into it. Reaching out, I grasped the doorknob and turned it. I expected it might be locked. But it wasn't although the door opened only a little way before it came to a stop against something heavy on the other side.

'What is it, Johnny?'

I swung round sharply. Dawn was standing beside me. 'I thought I told you to stay in the car,' I said harshly. 'You could've run into a hail of bullets back there.'

'You didn't,' she replied pointed. 'So I figured there was nobody at home.'

'There's somebody here,' I said. 'But somehow I don't think he'll be talking to us.' I pushed harder at the door until I was able to slip inside.

The interior was dark in contrast to the brilliant sunlight outside and for a few moments I had to wait until my eyes adjusted to the dimness. As I'd figured there was a body lying face down on the floor just inside the door. As Dawn squeezed her way in I turned the body over with my foot. I'd never seen the guy before but I reckoned he was one of Malloy's men. There was blood on his vest and the two neat holes testified that he'd been shot twice from fairly close range.

Leaving him, I made my way along the wide corridor with Dawn close on my heels. A door led into a large airy room.

Nothing seemed to have been disturbed but there were two more stiffs there spoiling the look of the carpet.

'Somebody must've had a field day here,' I remarked, 'and I'd say it was someone they knew. It wouldn't have been easy to take Malloy's men off guard like this.'

'And where's Malloy?' Dawn asked. 'You don't think they were trying to double-cross him and he shot them?'

The possibility hadn't occurred to me but I turned it over in my mind as I went into the next room, which was evidently the bedroom. There was someone lying on the bed and one look told me that Dawn's suggestion was wrong.

It was Shaun Malloy and he had gone the same way as the others. He lay there on his back staring up at the ceiling but seeing nothing.

I pushed my hat back on my head and looked across at Dawn. 'This case is getting screwier by the minute. The only one I can think of who'd do something like this is Rizzio. Yet that doesn't fit either. If some of his boys had driven out here to get rid of Malloy they'd have sprayed the place with bullets from outside. But there are no smashed windows — nothing. Whoever did this must have been inside the house for these stiffs to be where they are.'

'What do you think we should do, Johnny?'

I reached a decision right away. 'I reckon we should let O'Leary know what we've found. I don't envy his job trying to find out the identity of this killer. There has to be a phone around here someplace. We'll just have to pray that whoever did this didn't take the trouble to cut the line.'

There was a telephone on the table in the large front room. I took out my handkerchief and covered my hand as I picked up the receiver. I didn't want my prints all over it. I dialled O'Leary's number. He answered at once.

'Merak here, Lieutenant,' I said. 'I reckon you'd better get out to Malloy's beach house as quickly as you can. There's been four killings and one of them is Shaun Malloy.'

There was a long pause. Maybe he was wondering if this was a joke on my part but then he figured it wasn't and snapped. 'Are you there at the moment, Merak?'

'I'm here.'

'Then stay there until I arrive. And don't touch anything.'

'I know the procedure, Lieutenant,' I said. I put the phone down.

Going outside, we sat in a couple of deck chairs and waited. We didn't have to wait long. O'Leary wasn't one for hanging around on a case like this. It was less than twenty minutes later that we picked up the wail of sirens in the distance and two police cars stopped just behind mine.

O'Leary's face bore the usual expression of resigned surprise as he came up to me. 'All right, Merak. As usual I find you right in the middle of a crime scene. You say that Malloy is dead?'

'That's right. He's on the bed in the far room. One guy is just behind the front door and there are two others in the front room.'

'And I suppose we'll find your prints over nearly everything.'

I shook my head. 'Once I found that stiff lying behind the front door I figured there was something here you'd need to see. You might find Dawn's prints on the door handles but that's all. Neither of us expected to find anything like this when we came.'

'And just why did you come here? Far as I know, Malloy wasn't a particular friend of yours.' He gave me a sharp look as he motioned Kolowinski and the other two cops inside.

'I wanted to ask him a few questions concerning this case. I'd already eliminated Rizzio from these killings.'

Holding out his hand, he snapped, 'Let me see your gun, Merak.'

I handed the .38 over. He checked it carefully and sniffed it before handing it back. Then he swung on Dawn. 'Better hand over the one you're carrying, Miss Grahame. It would seem to me you were both expecting trouble.' He repeated the procedure with the Luger and then gave it back. 'All right. I'm satisfied you didn't kill whoever's in there.'

He made to follow the cops into the house. Over his shoulder he said dryly, 'Well, if Malloy is dead as you say, Rizzio is top of my list of suspects.'

When he came out again he didn't look too happy. 'Two of those guys had guns in their hands when they were shot,' he said thinly. 'Evidently they were taken completely by surprise and didn't have a chance to use them.'

'Doesn't that let Rizzio off the hook?' I asked. 'Those guys in there would know his boys the moment they saw them. This doesn't look like a gang killing to me.'

'So what are you suggesting? That this is the work of an outsider?'

'That's how it looks to me, Lieutenant. It had to be someone they knew. Someone they never expected would pull a gun and shoot them all down before they could defend themselves.'

He looked as if the whole weight of the world had suddenly dropped onto his shoulders. Kolowinski suddenly spoke up. 'I suppose you realize that you and your lady friend here could fit that bill, Johnny.'

'Sure we could. But you've already determined that our guns haven't been fired.'

'All right.' O'Leary snapped. It was obvious this case was beginning to get to him.

'You can both go. It's obvious that Malloy isn't going to answer any of your questions now. But don't leave town — either of you. There are a lot more questions I want to ask after we've finished here.'

We got back into the car leaving him staring after us as though wondering if it had been the right thing to let us go.

Dawn seemed unusually quiet as we headed back and I could tell she had something on her mind. It wasn't until we were entering the outskirts of the city that she said, 'I've been thinking, Johnny. You seem pretty sure that Somerville is dealing with Malloy but he'll have to change his plans once he learns that Malloy is dead. Don't you think it might be a good idea if we were to keep a watch on Somerville? Sooner or later, he's going to contact whoever he's dealing with and then you've got your answer.'

She was right, of course. 'Why the hell didn't I think of that before? I've been going at this from the wrong end. Do you have any idea where Herbert Somerville lives?'

'It won't take me long to find out. Pull up at the nearest phone booth.'

I did so and true to her word she came back with his address within five minutes. It was a place a little way to the north of the city, close to the coast. With Dawn sitting beside me, we drove out along the coastal highway. There was very little traffic apart from the usual huge trucks carrying fish to the canneries and we reached our destination half an hour later.

I'd figured Somerville as a guy who liked his solitude, just like Malloy, but I never expected a place like this. It was scarcely visible from the road set back almost half a mile and almost completely surrounded by trees. There was a pair of ornate iron gates and a wide drive leading into the distance.

Dawn stared at it in obvious amazement. 'I'd say he doesn't like mixing with people, living out there,' she remarked. 'And with that wall all around the place, my guess is that those gates are the only way in.'

I nodded. 'I'd also guess that the wire along the top of that wall is electrified. The place is more like a fortress than a house. Still it gives us one advantage.'

'What's that?' she asked.

'If there's only one way out he'll have to leave through those gates. All we do now is wait here until he puts in an appearance and then tail him. But it may be a long wait.'

It proved to be just that. After I'd driven the Merc a little further along the road and then turned off into a small verge screened by tall bushes, we settled down, keeping our eyes on the long drive leading to the mansion. Nearly two hours passed and I was getting impatient. I didn't like sitting in one place doing nothing. I had to be on the move where the action was.

I'd just glanced at my watch for what

seemed the hundredth time when Dawn nudged me. Looking up quickly I saw that someone had come out of the mansion and was getting into one of the cars at the end of the drive.

'Well now,' I said harshly, 'it looks as if he's finally on the move.' I switched on the ignition. I wasn't sure yet if it was Somerville driving that car but as it came closer to the gates, I was able to make out his bulky figure sitting behind the wheel.

'That's him all right,' I said.

The car was less than twenty yards from the gates when they swung open automatically. As Somerville drove out onto the road the gates closed again behind him just as noiselessly.

I waited until he was some distance away, almost out of sight, and then edged out and followed him at a discreet distance. I doubted if much traffic ever used this stretch of road and I didn't want him to get suspicious. However, he gave no sign that he was aware we were tailing him.

'He seems to be heading towards the east of town,' Dawn remarked suddenly.

'Do any of the godfathers live in that area?'

'Only one that I know of — Malloy. Most of the others live along the west coast. It's beginning to look as though we were right.'

'So what's your plan if we do track him to Malloy?'

'I guess I've got two choices. Either I get on the phone and let Manzelli know — or for the time being I do nothing. I still don't know who's threatening Edith Somerville's life. My money was on either Malloy or Herbert Somerville.'

'Perhaps both of them were working together,' Dawn suggested.

'Could be. Either way I'd have preferred both of these guys alive. If Manzelli were to decide to eliminate Somerville I'll never get the proof who's responsible for sending these flowers to Edith.'

We were now driving through the afternoon traffic but Somerville's limousine was quite easy to keep in sight. Once or twice I allowed some other car to get between us.

He gave no indication that he was aware of us on his tail but I was taking no chances. So far this was the best lead we had and I didn't want anything to foul it up.

At the third intersection he turned. There was now no doubt in my mind that he was heading for the suburbs. This was a part of town where only the very wealthy could afford to live. Directors and movie stars from the film studios and the occasional guy like Malloy who hid his true character behind a façade of luxurious respectability.

About half a mile further on, Somerville suddenly slowed and a moment later the car swung right between two massive iron gates that had opened at his approach. Evidently he was expected. The gates closed again once he was inside. I drove past, noticing the two guys who stood just inside the entrance, and parked fifty yards beyond the house.

'You think that's Malloy's place?' Dawn asked quietly.

'I know damned well it is,' I told her. 'He's the only one of the Big Bosses who lives in this area. He seems to have an obsession about people living close to him when he's in town. It's only when he's out at the summer place that he prefers solitude.

'We know there were a lot of guys in the outfits who were against him becoming the boss in his uncle's place. Some figured he was too young to stand up to the other bosses in the Organization. We know what happened to them and now to him.'

Twisting in my seat I looked back through the rear window. I could just make out Somerville as he got out of his car. There was a bulky envelope in his hand. He had only just reached the front door when it opened and a guy stood in the doorway. I recognized him as Dan Linney, Malloy's second-in-command.

Somerville seemed surprised and on the point of refusing to hand over the package. Linney caught him by the arm and said something and after a moment they both went inside.

'Somerville didn't seem very pleased,' I remarked. 'And what's the betting there was quite a nice sum of money in that envelope?'

'I'd say they're pretty good,' Dawn said, nodding. 'So now we know that Somerville and this outfit are working together what do you intend to do? Are you going to pass the word to Manzelli? He's sure to hear of Malloy's murder pretty soon.'

I knew that was what I should do. No one fooled around with Manzelli if they wanted to go on living. But those little mice were telling me to keep this to myself — at least for the time being. And this time I decided to listen to them. I shook my head. 'Not for the moment, Dawn. All we know is that they're working together but that doesn't help us to find the guy who killed Mrs. Somerville and has made these threats against her daughter.'

She gave me a worried look. 'Manzelli won't like that if he finds out you're holding out on him.'

'I know. I'm just hoping he won't get to hear of it until I've solved this case.' It was a dangerous game I was playing.

Manzelli had a habit of knowing everything that went on in L.A.

We waited. Clearly the two men had a lot of talking to do. It was almost an hour later when the front door opened and the two men came out. The envelope was now nowhere in sight. Malloy got back into his car and a moment later drove out into the street. The gates closed.

'Are you going to follow him?' Dawn asked as I waited until he was out of sight before turning the Merc.

'There's no need to do that. He's either headed back home or to the bank's head office. Besides, we already know who he's working with though he seemed surprised to find Malloy wasn't there. I've no doubt he's now aware that Malloy is dead. I think we can eliminate him from having any part in his murder. However, there's just one thing that puzzles me.'

'Oh, what's that?'

'How he's getting away with taking all that dough from the bank without being found out? I'm damned sure none of it is from his own personal fortune. He must be covering it up somehow.'

Dawn thought for a moment and then said, 'Perhaps if you had a word with Harry Grenville. He might be able to make a few inquiries.'

'I'll do that as soon as we get back to the office.'

Grenville was out of the office when I phoned him twenty minutes later but he called back in ten minutes. 'Have you got anything, Johnny?' he asked.

'I'm not quite sure how important it might be but Shaun Malloy and three of his men were shot down at his beach house. O'Leary is there right now. In the meantime I tailed Herbert Somerville to Malloy's town house. He had a large envelope with him when he went in but it was gone when he came out. It could have been a payoff.'

Grenville was silent for a few moments, evidently turning that idea over in his mind. Then he said, 'Why the hell is Somerville so anxious to buy himself into the Organization? Most folk want out.'

'Power, perhaps. It can't be dough he's after. He has enough to last him three lifetimes. But the reason I rang you,

Harry, is to ask if you can get details of Somerville's bank statements.'

'Any particular reason you need those?'

'If possible I'd like to know if the dough he's giving that gang is his own or if we can get him for embezzlement. If we can it would give us a chance to grill him.'

There was a low whistle at the other end of the line before he said, 'I might be able to get a court order to do that but I'd need some pretty strong evidence to convince a judge.'

'Can I leave it with you, Harry? Right now I'm hoping to be able to concentrate on Edith Somerville's case. I seem to have been neglecting her for the past few days and if whoever wrote that note means what he says, there are only a few days left.'

'All right, Johnny. I'll let you know immediately I find anything about Herbert Somerville.' There was a click and the line went dead.

I was just getting ready to drive out to the Ocean View hotel with my fingers around the door handle when there was a knock on the door. Opening it, I found Edith Somerville standing there. She was clearly scared and kept looking behind her as if expecting someone to be following her.

'Come in,' I said, motioning her to the chair in front of the desk. I replaced my hat on the peg. 'I was just on my way to see you.'

'Why? Have you discovered who's sending these roses? As I expected, there were eight this morning. Whoever it is, he means what he says.'

'No, I'm afraid not. But my assistant and I did discover something today which I think you should know about.'

She looked across at me, obviously puzzled. 'What would that be?'

'We followed your uncle. He drove straight to the house owned by one of the bosses in the Organization. He took a large envelope with him, which we believe contained a large sum of money. I'm sorry to have to tell you this but it's pretty certain he's in deep with these crooks.'

'I see.' She bit her lower lip but that

was the only sign she gave to indicate any surprise.

Either she already knew or had suspected it for some time. There was, however, something else on her mind now but I had the feeling she didn't want to come out with it. Finally, she said in a low voice, 'Do you think my uncle has made this threat against me?'

'I guess it's possible but we've got no real evidence of it.' I knew that Herbert Somerville was a ruthless and determined man. But was he the type to kill those others and subject his own niece to this mental torture before killing her too? Somehow, I didn't think so but it was certainly something worth considering.

Dawn brought over a cup of hot, strong coffee and placed it on the desk in front of her. She drank it slowly, grimacing a little as it burned her throat. Finally, she said, 'I've been through everyone I can think of who might want to kill me. But there's no one except possibly — ' She broke off as if this was something she didn't want to talk about.

'Go on,' I urged, leaning forward over

the desk. 'If there is someone, the sooner I know about it, the more chance I have of solving this case.'

She bit her lower lip, clearly ill at ease. Then she went on in a voice so low I could barely make out the words. 'There was someone but it was all a long time ago and I've almost forgotten him.'

'Someone you were in love with?' Dawn spoke for the first time.

Edith nodded. 'Yes. It was more than ten years ago. We were together for almost four years and were talking about marriage but then I began to suspect he was seeing other women behind my back.'

'So you hired someone to check on him?' I said.

'That's right. This was all long before the big fight between my father and uncle. This man, his name was David Franton, knew I was quite wealthy at that time — and there was the Somerville name of course. He probably knew that I'd inherit quite a fortune once my father died.'

'And what happened when you found out about his philandering?' Dawn asked.

'Naturally I broke off our relationship.'

I took out my pack of cigarettes and offered her one. When she shook her head, I lit one and sat back. 'How did he take that?'

'Very badly. That was when I saw a side of him I'd never seen before. He swore that if he couldn't have me nobody would.'

Through the smoke, I said, 'Why didn't you tell me all this before? It throws a new light on everything.'

She sat quite still staring down at her hands before replying. 'I suppose that since it all happened so long ago and I've never seen or heard from him since, I thought it wasn't relevant.'

She seemed on the verge of tears and Dawn got up and handed her a tissue. Dabbing her eyes, she said, 'If he's the one doing all of this, why would he kill my father and mother? They had no part in our break up.'

'Who knows how these people think? Do you know where he is now?'

She shook her head. 'As I said, I've had no contact with him for nearly six years.

He could be anywhere, married perhaps. He might even be dead by now. Do you think this is really important?'

'Every bit of information is important,' I told her. 'Unfortunately, after this length of time, it's not going to be easy to get anything on his present whereabouts but if he's still alive I'll find him.'

When she'd gone, I asked Dawn to make me more coffee. I needed it to clear my head. This new piece of information had thrown me completely. I'd felt certain these threats that Edith had been receiving came from someone in Malloy's mob, maybe even Malloy himself. Now I wasn't so sure.

'You look worried, Johnny,' Dawn said as she placed the coffee in front of me.

Frowning, I replied, 'Why the hell didn't she mention this guy Franton before? We've wasted days of precious time placing these murders on the Organization while all the time there's been this fellow lurking in her background.'

'Maybe she's right. Do you think it's likely he'd wait all this time before carrying out his threat? Besides, people often say things they don't really mean when they're angry. It could be just something said in the heat of the moment when she turned him down.'

I tried to tell myself that was exactly what it was, just some remark made to scare her. But for some reason I didn't have much success. Those little mice were really having a field day now, careering around, telling me that I should stick with my hunch — that this was one loose string that had to be examined and tied up.

'I want you to see if you can find out anything about this guy David Franton,' I said, swinging my legs off the desk. 'There's something here that doesn't sit right.'

'I don't understand, Johnny. Like she said, it was just something that was said a long time ago and — '

'Then why do I get the feeling that she meant to give us that piece of information but not until now when there's so little time left for her? Can we be sure it's true, that she hasn't made it all up just to confuse the issue.'

Dawn stared at me. 'Now you're not making any sense at all. Why should she do that?'

'I think she's had this man Franton on her mind for some time but for some reason she's decided not to tell us about him until now.'

Dawn shrugged. She still thought I was talking nonsense. 'I'll see if I can find out anything about him,' she said. 'But it'll be like searching for the needle in the proverbial haystack.'

'I know you'll do your best, Dawn. In the meantime I'll have a word with a few contacts I have. They might know something.'

There were a couple of guys I'd known during my days in the Organization. If Franton had ever come to the notice of any of the Mobs I felt sure they'd know. Whether they'd still talk to me now that I'd gone legit was debatable.

★ ★ ★

The first guy I went looking for had unfortunately died two years earlier. I was disappointed but I guess that's how it happens when you haven't seen your old acquaintances for some time.

I came upon my second contact sitting, or rather lying, on a park bench. He wasn't in a much better state than the first one but at least he was alive and, I hoped, capable of talking to me. Where he spent his nights I didn't know but it would be somewhere out of sight of any patrolling cops. Paulo Buletti had once been a big man in the Organization running his own rackets, mostly protection and drug dealing. Then his life had been a lush mansion and a round of girls and fast cars. But he'd made the mistake of wanting more and trying to double cross Carlos Galecci, boss of the biggest outfit in L.A. Normally he'd have been found lying face-down in an alley someplace but this time Galecci must have been feeling generous for his boys just did him over. Now he existed with a busted kidney on handouts from anyone who felt sorry for him.

Looking at him now, I had the feeling he'd have been better off with a slug in him. At least it would have been quick and virtually painless. He stared up at me out of watery blue eyes, blinking in the strong sunlight. Then something came into his eyes and his mouth opened in a toothless grin.

'My God!' he mumbled. 'Johnny Merak. Where the hell have you been all these years? When you pulled out of the Mob I figured they'd either kill you or leave you like this.' He pointed a shaking finger at himself.

I sat down beside him. He was a total wreck of a man and I wasn't sure just how much I could rely on anything he said. But at least he remembered me and that was something.

'I need some information Paulo and I figure you might be able to give me it.'

Grabbing the back of the seat with one hand he pulled himself into a sitting position. His wrinkled features twisted into a grimace as if the smallest movement gave him a lot of pain. He looked around to see if there was anyone in the vicinity.

'Anything for an old pal, Johnny,' he muttered.

I took a ten spot from my wallet and waved it in front of him. 'This is yours if you give me anything useful.'

'What is it you want to know?' He ran his tongue around his lips. I reckoned he hadn't had a decent meal for days and the sight of the ten dollar bill seemed to mesmerize him.

'You knew nearly everyone in all of the outfits in the old days, Paulo. Did you ever come across a guy named David Franton?'

'Franton.' He mouthed the word as if he were chewing on it. Then he shook his head slowly. 'Can't say there was ever anyone of that name in any of the outfits I knew.'

'You're absolutely certain?' I hadn't expected to learn anything worthwhile at my second attempt. Nonetheless, I experienced a sense of disappointment.

'Yeah, I'm sure.' He hesitated for a moment, still staring at the bill in my hand. 'But somehow the name sounds familiar. David Franton.' He repeated the name to himself, scratching the stubble on his chin.

When he said nothing more, I got to my feet. Then I thrust the dough into his hand. I'd learned nothing — but what the hell! I figured he needed it more than I did. Turning, I walked away; then stopped as he called in a cracked voice, 'Wait, Johnny! I've just remembered. There was a David Franton but he wasn't in the Organization. He was a cop.'

I went back to him, gripping his arm tightly. 'You're telling me this guy was in the LAPD?'

'That's right. Pretty high up too from what I remember.'

'Do you know what happened to him — where he is now?'

'Far as I've heard he's still a cop. But if I were you I'd steer clear of him.'

'Why?'

'He's a nasty piece of work. Anyone he picks up can be sure of a beating up before they get to the precinct. You can take that as gospel. I've been in the police car with him and I know what I'm talking about. He always carries a piece of rubber hose with him. Of course, he makes damned sure the bruises aren't anywhere you can see them.'

I nodded. 'I get the picture. Thanks Paulo. You've been a great help.' I thrust a second ten-dollar bill into his hand. I figured that it was worth it.

What I'd just been told certainly tallied with what Edith had said about Franton. He was a guy with a violent temper. Naturally, I had to take Paulo's information with a certain degree of caution. This guy in the LAPD might not be the one I was looking for but at least it was a lead. It was also possible that Jack Kolowinski might know him and could fill me in on a few details.

I wasn't sure whether or not Jack was on duty so I decided to go along to the precinct and check. Jack was at the desk when I went in. He seemed to be engaged in a one-way dialogue with an elderly woman. Evidently she had lost her dog and wanted him to go out and search for it that very minute. I waited until he managed to pass her on to someone else.

As I'd expected, he was surprised to see me there. Normally, I kept as far away from the precinct as possible. Cops, and in particular Lieutenant O'Leary tended to have an inbred dislike of private investigators. It was just something that went with the job, I guess.

'If you're looking for the Lieutenant,' he began, 'he's — '

'I doubt if he'll give me much help,' I said. 'I just wanted to ask you if there's a cop here by the name of Franton.'

'Sure. He's a lieutenant in the drugs squad. What did you want to see him for? One of your clients been caught with a load of the white stuff?'

I shook my head and leaned forward over the desk. Lowering my voice, I said, 'It's to do with Edith Somerville. Apparently some guy called David Franton had a hankering for her about ten years ago but she eventually gave him the brush off. It just came into my mind that he might be the same guy.'

Kolowinski considered that for a moment. This was obviously something he didn't want to talk about, particularly to someone like me. I could understand his predicament, spilling the dirt on a colleague who was also his superior could be dangerous. O'Leary could be a hard man to rub along with but from what little I'd heard Franton could be a lot worse.

Finally, he made up his mind. In a low whisper, he said, 'Won't it wait until tonight, Johnny? I could meet you in Mancini's.'

'I'd prefer to hear it now if that's possible.'

'O.K. Come through into the interview room. We can talk in there.'

I followed him around the desk to a room at the back. Motioning me to the chair at the table, he sat down in the other. 'All right, Johnny,' he began, 'there isn't much I can tell you. Franton isn't liked in the force. He's a good cop and gets results but sometimes he goes over the score whenever he brings some suspects in. I've known women coming in with bruises on their bodies, claiming that he'd beaten them up.'

'Sure. But do you know anything about his liaison with Edith Somerville?'

'Not much. He very seldom said anything about it. In those days she was in line for quite a fortune and maybe it was that he was after. I'm not saying he beat her up or anything like that but I heard there were frequent quarrels, especially towards the end of their relationship.'

'What exactly happened when she broke it off?'

Kolowinski rubbed his chin and thought for a moment. 'As far as I can remember he took a holiday someplace. I know he was away from the precinct for about a month.'

'I see. Just one more thing, Jack. Would you say he's the kind of guy to harbour a grudge for six years?'

Kolowinski gave me a funny look. 'You're not suggesting that he's the one behind these murders and this threat against Edith Somerville?'

'In my job, like yours, I have to examine every possibility, no matter how remote or ridiculous it seems.'

'Well, I reckon that's about all I can tell you, Johnny.' He pushed back his chair and got up.

'You can do one thing more for me,' I said, following him to the door. 'If he's here at the moment I'd like you to point him out to me.'

Kolowinski paused and turned to face me. His expression was serious. 'Don't mess with him, Johnny. I'm just giving you a fair warning. He can make life hell for you if he reckons you're checking on him.'

I grinned. 'A lot of people have done that, Jack. I guess one more won't make much difference.'

Shrugging, he led the way towards the far side of the office. There were glass panels in the wall and through them I saw there was another room almost identical with the one in which I was standing. Most of the guys there were in plain clothes.

'That's Franton standing next to the little guy in the corner.'

The man he pointed out was tall and snappily dressed, his black hair sleeked back. He had a small moustache and there was a scar on his upper left cheek just below the eye. I stood there for a minute taking in every little detail of his face, making certain I'd know him again.

I'd always regarded O'Leary as a hard cop but there was something about Franton's eyes and the set of his thin lips that I didn't like. He suddenly glanced in my direction and instantly his eyes narrowed. He obviously didn't know me but he also didn't like being scrutinized by strangers.

'Satisfied?' Kolowinski asked.

I gave a nod. 'Thanks, Jack. I may be going down the wrong road with Franton but Edith Somerville never mentioned him until today and there's little time left. I'll let you know if anything turns up.'

I drove back to the office with those little mice racing around inside my head. Much of what Edith had told me was evidently true but why had she kept it to herself for so long? Did she really believe that, because it had all happened so long ago, Franton was irrelevant to this case?

Or had there been a deeper reason in her mind?

Dawn wasn't there when I arrived but she came in ten minutes later. Glancing across at me, she said, 'I hope you had better luck with your contacts than I had, Johnny. No one seems to know much about Franton.'

I lit a cigarette and sat back in my chair. 'Fortunately one of the guys I met seemed to know quite a lot about him. I had him figured for someone pretty high in the Organization but it turns out he's a cop. Not one of the best of cops but he's a lieutenant in the drugs squad.'

Dawn sat down. 'If he's a friend of O'Leary's it might make things difficult to find out much about him.'

'Jack Kolowinski filled me in on some of the details. He's well known for beating up any suspects before he gets them to the precinct. I suppose it's possible that Edith discovered this and it's the reason she rejected him.'

She pressed her lips together in concentration. 'So he's got an anger problem but do you think he's still sufficiently angry after all these years to make these threats against her? Why didn't he decide to torment her in this way all those years ago when she finished with him?'

'Perhaps he's being very clever. If she'd been murdered then he'd have been the number one suspect. He might not have got away with it.'

Dawn came over and sat on the edge of my desk. 'So we now have three possible suspects. Franton, Herbert Somerville or someone in the Organization.'

'Which means we're back at square one,' I said. 'This case is getting more complicated as time goes on. And unfortunately time is something we're desperately short of.'

I still wasn't certain about Franton, who seemed to have been brought into this case at the very last minute. At that moment, however, I didn't know just how much trouble Franton had in store for me. If I'd known it then, I might have changed my mind about him.

It wasn't until the next day that Franton showed his hand. Dawn and I arrived at the office at almost the same time. We'd only been there a couple of minutes, however, when the door opened. There'd been no polite knock. Maybe the three guys who came in didn't believe in any of the decent ways of going about things.

I recognized the first guy immediately from the previous day. It was Franton. The two men with him I'd never seen before.

Franton took something from his pocket and held it out to me. 'I believe I have the right place,' he said harshly. There was a touch of malice in his voice that I noticed at once. 'You are Johnny Merak, private investigator.'

I nodded, getting to my feet. 'That's my name.'

He pushed the piece of paper into my hand. 'This is a warrant signed by Judge Carruthers to search this office.'

'Perhaps I can help you if you tell me what it is you're looking for.' I saw Dawn looking at me with a quizzical expression on her face.

'We'll know if we find anything,' he said

shortly. 'In the meantime both of you remain just where you are.' He signalled to the two men with him.

It was soon clear these guys were experts. While one pulled out all the drawers in Dawn's desk, the other did likewise with mine. The cop next to me took out the Luger, turned it over in his hand, checking that it was loaded. Then he handed it to Franton.

'Do you have a permit for this weapon?' he asked.

I knew there was no point in lying. It would only take these guys five minutes to check. I shook my head. 'Not that one,' I told him. 'It's been in my desk for years. I do have a permit for this one.' I pulled aside my jacket to show the .38 in its holster.

'I suppose you know it's a felony to possess an unregistered weapon?' There was a malicious smile on his lips. However, I had the feeling they weren't looking for any weapons I might have. All I'd get for that was a fine and the weapon confiscated. That wasn't what he wanted.

Before he could say anything further

there came a sudden call from the guy who'd been rummaging unnoticed through my filing cabinet. He held out a small package, which contained something I didn't recognize.

Franton took it and his smile widened as he opened it, pushed his forefinger into it and touched it to his tongue. One of the men produced a plastic bag and he dropped the package into it.

Facing me, he said thinly, 'It would appear that our information was correct, Merak. I'm arresting you for illegal possession of cocaine.' Turning to one of his companions, he said, 'Read him his rights, sergeant, and then we'll take him down to the precinct — the woman as well. My guess is they're both in this together.'

'Just a minute,' I interrupted. 'I know a shakedown when I see one. That package wasn't in there yesterday. Either you or one of your squad got into the office through the night or he slipped it in there just now.'

'Sure,' Franton nodded. 'Isn't it strange? Everyone says that when they're caught in possession of illegal drugs. Now both of you come with us. We'll see what the captain says about this. One thing's for sure. Neither of you will be doing any investigating for quite a while.'

There was nothing either of us could do as they put on the cuffs and led us outside. I cursed myself inwardly for not seeing this coming. This was one mess I couldn't see a way out of. It hadn't taken Franton long to recognize someone who might pose a threat to him. Whether he thought I was about to finger him for murder, I didn't know. But he couldn't have acted faster if he'd been on skates.

My only hope now was that Manzelli would learn about this and somehow put the pressure on those higher up than Franton.

There were two police cars waiting outside and we were led towards them. Dawn was pushed into the seat beside the driver while Franton crashed into the back beside me. The other two cops got into the other car.

'All right, Ted.' Franton leaned forward and spoke to the driver. 'Back to the precinct but take the long way and drive real slow.'

I knew what was coming even before it happened and, with my hands cuffed, there was nothing I could do about it. Clenching his fist, Franton struck me a heavy blow behind the ear. I fell forward at the back of the driver's seat. Straightening up he slid his hand into his pocket. When it came out there was a short rubber cosh in it.

I'd been done over several times in the past but this guy was a professional at inflicting pain. He knew just the right places to hit. Somehow, I remained conscious. In front of me, Dawn screamed twice before Franton struck her savagely across the mouth.

The journey to the precinct was an agony of pain. The driver made no move to put a stop to it. No doubt he knew his job was on the line if he attempted to interfere. It was quite likely he'd seen it all before, many times.

The beating only stopped when we finally turned into the street where the precinct was situated. The car slid to a halt and I was hauled roughly out of the car. Once inside, Franton thrust me towards the desk There was no sign of Dawn and I figured that, for some reason, they meant to keep her in the car until they'd finished with me.

To the desk sergeant, Franton said harshly, 'I've brought this man in on a charge of being in possession of cocaine. His accomplice is outside in the car. I'll deal with her later.'

The sergeant looked me up and down and then said thinly, 'What happened to him, lieutenant?'

'Resisting arrest, sergeant. Unfortunately, I had to restrain him.'

I guessed from the expression on the other's face that he didn't believe him but he said nothing, merely taking down everything that Franton told him.

'He's lying.' Somehow, I got the words out. 'This was a plant. And if he thinks that by beating me up in the car is going to make me confess, he'd better think again. I don't scare that easily.'

'You'll talk by the time I'm finished with you, Merak,' Franton almost snarled the words. He made no attempt to deny what I said about the beating. 'In the meantime put him into one of the cells.' He walked off leaving me in the custody of the sergeant who made to move around the desk.

'Don't I get to make one phone call?' I asked.

'Sure. But where Franton is concerned, I don't reckon there's anyone who can help you.' He studied me closely for a moment. 'Believe me, Merak, I don't like this any more than you do. And I don't believe for one minute that a friend of Jack Kolowinski's had any illegal drugs. If it's any consolation, I'm damned sure he planted that incriminating evidence on you and I guess most of the honest coppers here agree with me.' He pushed the telephone towards me. 'One call,' he said, moving back.

I rang Manzelli's number. I knew I was taking a big chance and that no one ever got in touch with Manzelli himself. But I was hoping one of his henchmen would answer and somehow get the message to him. A lot was going to depend how badly he wanted this case solved. A voice I didn't recognize answered the call. Briefly I explained what had happened and asked whoever it was if he'd get in touch with his boss. The guy said he'd pass the word to Manzelli and then the line went dead.

6

Manzelli Steps In

Five minutes later I was shown into a small cell and the door shut with a clang like the trump of doom. I sat down on the small bench and tried to think things through, logically and coherently. Evidently Franton had recognized me at once the previous day. The fact that he had acted so drastically and precipitously indicated there was something in his past he was afraid I'd discover. Even if I proved myself innocent, which seemed highly unlikely, the dirt would still cling and somehow discredit me as a witness if he ever came to trial. He'd also make certain that Dawn got the same treatment.

The desk sergeant had left me my cigarettes and lighter which was a nice touch on his part. I lit a cigarette and blew the smoke into the air as I tried to figure out what the chances were that Manzelli would do something to get Dawn and me out of this mess. He'd done it before when Sam Rizzio, boss of the biggest outfit had put out a hit on me but that was only because it suited his purpose at the time. Whether he would do it now was in the lap of the gods.

The hands on my watch crawled around the face as if not wanting to move. I wondered what was happening with Dawn. My guess was that Franton was questioning her somewhere in this building. I didn't doubt that she would stick to the truth no matter what kind of grilling they gave her. She was that kind of woman. Franton wouldn't find it easy to scare her into making a false confession.

By the time another hour passed I was beginning to think I'd be there until hell froze over. There was no sound from outside the cell door. I went over to it and yelled: 'Anybody out there. I'd like a drink of water.'

There was no answer to my shout. I tried again and then gave it up. Either they'd forgotten all about me or Franton was trying to soften me up. Then, ten minutes later a key grated in the lock and the door opened. Someone came in. It was Harry Grenville. He had a cup of hot coffee in his hand.

'You seem to have got yourself into a real mess this time, Johnny,' he said, sitting down on the bunk beside me.

'My own fault, Harry,' I said, sipping the coffee slowly. 'I should have foreseen that Franton might try something like this. He recognized me yesterday and it didn't take him long to find out who I am. Evidently he's got some reason to be scared I might find out something about him. Is there anything you can do to get me out of here?'

He hesitated; then shook his head. 'There's not much the FBI can do, I'm afraid, Johnny. Even though drugs are concerned, this is a purely local issue and since all of the evidence seems to be against you, Franton has got you exactly where he wants you.'

'But you know I've never been involved with drugs in my life. This was a plant.

That other cop brought that cocaine with him and just pulled it out of the filing cabinet like a magician pulling a rabbit from a hat.'

'I believe you, Johnny. From what I know of Franton, he does this all the time. If he can't find the evidence he wants, he puts it there himself. But no one's been able to prove it.' Grenville got up and moved towards the door. 'I'll do all I can to get you out of this, Johnny, but don't get your hopes up. It may be that — '

He broke off as the door opened. Two guys stood there. Their faces were vaguely familiar but I couldn't remember where I'd seen them before. One thing was for sure. They weren't cops. These were men from the Organization. I felt a little trickle of sweat run down between my shoulder blades.

'All right, Merak,' said the first guy, 'Your assistant is waiting for you outside. Finish your coffee and then come with us.'

I got slowly to my feet. This was something I couldn't understand — unless Franton had sent these men and Dawn and I were being taken elsewhere, some place where there were no witnesses around.

'What do you mean, she's waiting outside? Where are we going?'

What might have passed for a smile crossed the other's features. He glanced obliquely in Grenville's direction. He evidently knew the other was a Federal agent but it didn't seem to bother him. 'I guess you can go where the hell you like,' he said. 'It seems someone has been in touch with Judge Carruthers and the D.A. Both of them have decided there isn't enough evidence to support Lieutenant Franton's charge of you being in possession of illegal drugs. The D.A. has ordered it to be dropped. You're both free. We're here just to make sure you don't run into any trouble leaving.'

I tried to concentrate on what he was saying but his words seemed to go over the top of my head without registering on my brain. It took a couple of minutes for me to realize just how this had come about. There was only one man in L.A. who could swing it with both a judge and the D.A. Evidently my phone call to Manzelli had paid off.

As I stepped out of the cell, Grenville muttered softly, 'It would seem you've got some very powerful friends here, Johnny.'

'True, Harry. But believe me there'll be a price to pay for this favour.'

We went outside. There was no sign of Franton as we passed through the office. Maybe, I thought, he was with Judge Carruthers being lectured on the foolishness of trying to plant evidence on innocent people.

Dawn was there waiting. When she saw me she ran forward and threw her arms around my neck and kissed me. 'I thought we'd never get out of there,' she said finally. 'What happened, Johnny? All I could gather was that the D.A. and some judge had decided there wasn't sufficient evidence and the charge was to be dropped. Someone must have got to them.'

'Someone did,' I told her as we walked towards the waiting limousine. 'Don't you recognize this car?'

She stared at it for a moment and then

at the two guys waiting beside it. Turning to face me she whispered, 'Manzelli?'

I nodded. 'It would seem he wants to keep me in circulation for a while and somehow solve this case. I've no doubt he has quite a lot of dirt on Carruthers, and enough on the D.A. to make them do just as he wants.'

We got into the car and for the first time in my life I felt quite happy to ride with these two guys. They dropped us off outside my office.

'I never thought I'd see the old place again,' I said as I unlocked the door. 'I was sure Franton had sewn us up tighter than the Hoover Dam.'

Sinking into my chair I took out the bottle of whiskey from the drawer together with a couple of glasses. Holding up one to Dawn she hesitated and then gave a quick nod. 'I think we deserve a drink after what's happened,' she said. A worried frown suddenly creased her forehead. 'Do you think Franton will give up now?'

I took a sip of my drink. 'Somehow I don't think so. My guess is that he's running scared of what I might uncover in his past. Once he figures out that someone got to Carruthers, he'll try something else. He's a dangerous man and capable of just about anything.'

'Even murder?' Dawn asked in a low whisper.

'Yes, even that. I've already got him figured as the number one suspect for the killing of Edith's father and mother. One more killing won't make much difference to him.' I realized this was the first time I'd openly made my suspicions about Franton known to Dawn.

'I have the feeling neither her father or mother approved of him. They probably knew more about him beating her up than we figured and if they threatened to expose him as a woman beater it wouldn't do his career any favours.'

'And you think that's a strong enough motive for murder?'

'I've known murders committed for much less, Dawn,' I said solemnly. I knew there were probably flaws in my argument but more and more I was coming round to the view that Franton was our killer.

The trouble was it wasn't going to be easy to prove it. He now knew I had some important friends on my side and I'd be watching his every move from now on. He'd suffered a setback but that only made him all the more dangerous.

But while he had his problems — I had mine. Time was now running out for Edith Somerville and if I were to help her and save her life it was imperative I should find out a lot more about David Franton.

Finishing my drink I said, 'I'd like you to find out as much as you can about this guy Franton. But be careful. I don't want to alert him to the fact that we're investigating him. About all we know for certain is that he's head of the drug squad and likes beating up suspects before he gets them to the precinct. I'd like to get my hands on the police records for several years back but that won't be easy.

'I could ask Jack Kolowinski but since he's in Homicide he'd find himself in big trouble if he started asking about the records for the Drug Squad. Not only that but it wouldn't take Franton long to find out and he'd know at once who'd asked Jack to do it.'

'Could O'Leary help?'

'Not a chance, I'm afraid. O'Leary hates my guts almost as much as Franton. But there might be someone who may be able to give me some information that could prove useful.'

'And, of course, he'll be another friend of yours from the old gangland days?' Dawn said. She had that worried look on her face again.

'You could say that although I doubt if he looks on me as a friend since the last time we met was in San Quentin.'

★ ★ ★

Eddie Denson was a punk. He was also one of the lucky ones. Some time before he'd been picked up by the cops on a charge of suspected murder and drug peddling. Two other guys, both high up in the Organization, had been arrested with him but Eddie had been offered a plea bargain by the D.A. All he had to do was

164

testify against his two colleagues and he'd get off with a far lesser sentence and the offer of being placed in a protection programme once he got out.

But Denson hadn't squealed and for that he got ten years. The Organization never forgot what he did. Once he'd done his time he got the best. A big house and a flash car and all the dough he needed for the high life. In his turn, Denson never forgot the guy who'd arrested him — David Franton.

I was relying on his hatred of Franton to get some information out of him. It was possible he wouldn't talk to me. But that was a chance I had to take. I knew his usual haunts, the casinos along the front and that was where I went looking for him. It was something of a long shot since he was one of the night people, seldom seen around during the daylight hours.

Fortunately, luck was with me that day. I found him in the third place I went into. He was seated at one of the roulette tables with a couple of his boys at his back and a tall blonde immediately behind him. He was laughing and joking with the dame and some of the others at the table so I figured he'd had a run of good luck. I walked over until I was standing a couple of feet from the nearest bruiser.

'Hello, Eddie,' I said. 'You seem to have hit a lucky streak.'

He turned his head slowly, staring at me as if I'd just popped up out of the floor. I'd taken him by surprise and he was wondering who the hell I was. Then recognition came. Taking the large cigar from his mouth, he said, 'Johnny Merak. What the hell are you doing here? I heard you'd pulled out of the Organization and turned legit. You're some kind of private dick they tell me.'

Nodding, I said, 'That's right, Eddie.'

'So what are you doing in a joint like this? The investigation business must be paying you well if you can afford the kind of stakes they have here.'

'I came here looking for you.'

He suddenly snapped his fingers. His cigar had gone out. The dame at his back took her arm from around his neck and picked up a gold lighter from the table. Bending forward she relit it for him.

Puffing on it, he said tersely, 'What do you want with me, Merak? At the moment I've no need of a private detective.'

I threw a quick glance at the two guys with him. I knew it would only take one wrong word from me and I'd be hustled out of there and tossed into the street.

Choosing my words carefully, I said, 'I'd like to have a little talk about a mutual friend of ours — David Franton.'

'Franton!' He spat the word out as if it hurt his mouth. His hands on the table in front of him were suddenly clenched into fists. 'Why should I want to talk about that punk?'

'I'll tell you why. If I can get the right information, I may be able to have him put away for life.'

He turned his head at that and stared directly at me. I saw that I now had his attention. He still seemed to be debating inwardly as to whether or not I was being serious. He must have decided that I was deadly serious for he suddenly pushed back his chair. Pulling his chips to the edge of the table, he scooped them up and gave them to one of the guys. 'Cash these for me and then wait here.'

Jerking his thumb, he indicated that I was to follow him. Once we were standing at the far wall, out of earshot of any of the punters, he said shortly, 'What's all this about Franton?'

'I reckon you know he's now one of the top guys in the Drugs Squad of the LAPD.'

He nodded. 'I know that. He put me away for ten years. If you've got anything on him, spill it. I've waited a long time to get even with that punk.'

'At the moment I've nothing on him that would stand up in front of a jury, but — '

'Then why the hell are you here, wasting my time?' He spat the words out. 'You said you could have him put away for life.' He made to walk away.

'I said that and I meant it. But I need certain information and I think you can give me it.' I was talking to his retreating back but after a couple of steps, he halted and turned to face me. 'What sort of information?'

I had his attention again. 'Some years ago, Franton was going out with a woman called Edith Somerville but she broke off the relationship and he never forgave her for it.'

'So?'

'That was around the time he had you, and two others, arrested for murder and drug peddling. Tell me if I'm wrong but I believe that he was working closely with someone high up in the Underworld; someone who wanted the three of you out of the picture.'

Eddie pressed his lips together into a hard line. 'I don't know how you've figured that out, Merak, but that's the way I saw it at the time. It was Carlos Galecci that Franton was in with. The three of us had guessed there was something funny going on. We'd seen them together on a number of occasions. They used to meet on the same night every month.

'Then they must have found out we knew about these meetings but we couldn't prove it and our word wouldn't be accepted against Galecci's. The rest you know.'

This was the kind of information I wanted. There was, however, something more I needed to know. 'There's just one more thing, Eddie. This is important. Can you remember if there was another person in with Galecci and Franton?'

He scratched his chin, screwing up his lips, before replying. Then he nodded. 'You're right, there was. I'd completely forgotten about him because he wasn't a member of the Organization.'

'He wasn't?'

'No. I never found out who he was but I'd say he was a guy with plenty of dough.'

'A banker, perhaps?' I prompted.

'I guess he could've been.' He paused. 'Anything else you want to know? Now that Galecci's dead there's nothing I can do about him. But if what I've told you can put Franton away for life, I guess I owe you one.'

'Thanks, Eddie. You've been a great help.' I left the casino with those little mice scampering and chasing each other inside my head. Now I knew a lot of things that previously had merely been guesswork. I didn't doubt that this third guy who'd met with Galecci and Franton was Herbert Somerville. Little bits of the puzzle were beginning to fall into place and although they didn't make a nice picture, at least they were beginning to make some kind of sense.

Sliding behind the wheel of the Merc I turned the key in the ignition and pulled away into the main stream of traffic. I noticed this other car that pulled out a short distance behind me. For a little while I thought nothing of it but when it stuck to me like glue I started to get worried. Somebody had tailed me to the casino and now seemed determined not to lose me.

I kept my eye on him as I tried to figure out my next move. It would be an easy job to lose him, particularly in the heavy traffic around this part of town. But that wouldn't tell me anything — whether he was just another guy going the same way as myself or someone who had his own reasons for following me.

I decided to head for the outskirts of town where there would be much less traffic and I might be able to find answers to these questions.

Very soon, I was driving along the country road to the north of town. It was a landscape of hills and deep ravines. The road was narrow with sharply angled bends with white posts marking drop-offs that went down steeply for several hundred feet. There was very little traffic here. Most folk preferred the coast road. A few of the trucks used this one as a shorter route but that was all.

My shadowing friend was still behind me as I put the Merc to a steep upgrade. So far he'd kept his distance. If he had anything in mind I reckoned this was where he would make his play. There would be very few witnesses around and it would be easy for an accident to happen and go unreported for quite a while.

A heavy truck passed me going down the steep grade like a bat out of hell. Then, in the rear mirror I saw the car behind me suddenly surge forward as the driver put his foot down on the accelerator. I'd already figured what his intentions were — to drive me off the side into one of the ravines. Pushing down on the accelerator I headed for the top of the incline. A quick glance in the mirror told me he'd almost caught up with me.

The next second, he slammed into the rear of the Merc. Gripping the wheel tightly in both hands I managed to keep the car on the road. I'd met with this manouvre before and knew what to expect. I also knew this road well and had already figured out a way of getting this killer off my back. He dropped back a couple of hundred yards and then came on again. The impact rammed me hard against the wheel and for a split second the nearside tires slid onto the rocky verge. Somehow I managed to control the vehicle as it threatened to topple over on one side.

Then I was over the summit and speeding down the other side, my foot still on the accelerator. At the bottom was a right-angled bend marked by the line of white posts. Now, I told myself, everything depended on split second timing.

The car at my back speeded up again as I neared the bottom of the hill but this time he made no attempt to hit me in the rear. Instead, he moved out towards the far side of the road hoping to come up alongside me and then edge me over the side. It was then I noticed the large truck moving towards the bend from the other direction. My murderous companion had spotted it too for he immediately braked to get in behind me.

I was now right on the bend. Gripping the wheel I spun it sharply, praying that the Merc wouldn't go into a skid. It didn't. Somehow it clung to the road. Behind me, however, my pursuer evidently had his eyes on the truck for he clearly hadn't realized just how close he was to the steep left turn. I slammed my foot on the brakes as I saw what was happening behind me. The car went straight into the line of posts, smashing them into matchwood.

It sailed over the edge and seemed to hang there, suspended by invisible wires before it dropped out of sight. Bringing the Merc to a stop I got out and walked to the rim of the drop off. Turning over and over in midair, the vehicle smashed onto the rocks a couple of hundred feet below. There was a sudden flash of orange and the next moment it exploded in an expanding ball of flame but not before I'd seen the driver being thrown clear before it hit the ground.

I knew it wouldn't be easy getting down to where he was lying on a long ledge of rock but I needed to know who he was and why he'd been so determined to kill me. Very slowly, I lowered myself down. He was lying on his back when I reached him and one look was enough to tell me that he would soon be knocking on the Pearly Gates — or the other place.

'All right,' I said harshly, 'just who are you and who paid you to kill me?'

He drew his lips back across his teeth. 'Go to hell, Merak. I'm telling you nothing.'

'You're already just one step away from hell,' I told him. 'And evidently you know me so it's no use lying. My guess is you're working for the Organization or Herbert Somerville.'

'Okay. So I work for the Mobs but I've never had anything to do with Herbert Somerville.'

His voice was little more than a hoarse whisper now. Running his tongue around his lips, he muttered, 'I need a doctor. Get me to a hospital.'

I shook my head. 'You'd never make it. Just lie still and I'll try to get help.'

I edged away but he grabbed my sleeve. A shudder went through him and a thin trickle of blood dribbled from the side of his mouth. He swallowed thickly as he tried to get words out.

'It was . . . '

Before he could say anything more there was a low rattle in his throat and his head fell back onto the rocks. I'd been absolutely certain that either someone in the Mobs or Somerville had sent him to rub me out. But what he'd just said threw me for the moment.

I sat beside the dead man for a few minutes turning these revelations over in my mind. Then I began the difficult and treacherous climb back to the highway. It took me ten minutes to reach the top. When I got there I found a highway cop waiting for me.

He gave me a hand onto the road and then asked, 'What happened here?'

'I'm not sure,' I told him. 'He was following me down the hill and I guess he was travelling at much too high a speed for this road. He went through the barrier yonder and smashed onto the rocks down there.'

The cop held out his hand. 'You got any identification?'

I gave him my business card. He studied it for a few moments and then handed it back. 'A private investigator, eh?' His eyes narrowed. 'Are you sure he wasn't after you for some reason?'

'Why would he be after me?' I replied, forcing evenness into my voice. 'It's usually the other way around.'

'So what were you doing down there? Why didn't you get to a phone and report an accident?'

I thought fast. I could see this guy was getting more and more suspicious. 'I saw the car going down and just before it hit the rocks he was thrown clear. That's when I figured he might still be alive. If he was I might be able to do something for him.'

'And is he still alive?'

'No. He's dead all right.'

The cop considered that for a full minute before making up his mind. 'All right, Mister Merak. I'll report this and someone will bring his body up. I suppose I'll be able to contact you at the address on your card if there are any more questions I need to ask you.'

'I'll be there.'

Pushing his notebook back into his pocket, he gave me a nod and then walked back to his car. I waited until he'd gone before getting into the Merc and switching on the ignition.

7

The Wrong Man

How O'Leary would take this information about my being attacked, and my suspicions about who was behind it, I wasn't sure. I decided to drive back to the office and run it past him. I intended to phone him the moment I got in but it wasn't necessary. He was seated in the chair in front of my desk as I went in. Sergeant Kolowinski stood near the door looking more bored than usual. Dawn was sitting at her desk, a worried frown on her face.

'Been waiting long, Lieutenant?' I asked as I sat down.

'Long enough,' he snapped. 'Don't you ever spend any time in your office?'

'Not if I can help it,' I said. 'Most of my time is spent meeting people outside. But why are you here? I was going to phone you as soon as I got in.'

'Oh.' He didn't look too interested. 'Then I've saved you the trouble.'

Leaning forward, he placed his elbows on the desk and stared directly at me. 'I've just heard what happened at the precinct. It seems you've ruffled some feathers with the Drug Squad. Tell me, just what have you got against Lieutenant Franton? Or is this just some stupid game you're playing to get a bit of publicity?'

'Sure I'll tell you. He came storming into this office brandishing a search warrant and then one of his men planted some cocaine in the filing cabinet yonder and says he found it there. Franton then hauls Dawn and I down to the precinct but tells his driver to go the long way and take his time while he gives me the going over on the way.

'I get thrown into the slammer and left there for more than two hours. Then it seems Judge Carruthers and the D.A. reckon there isn't enough evidence against us and they let us go.'

'In other words you fixed it with Manzelli to get you out.'

'Now why should you say a thing like

that, Lieutenant? You know that Manzelli runs the whole of the L.A. Organization. I don't have anything to do with him.'

'Like hell you don't.' O'Leary leaned back in his seat. 'I don't know what your beef is with Franton but he's a damned good officer. People making accusations like this against him are doing the whole force a disservice.'

I took out a cigarette and lit it. 'Believe me, Lieutenant I don't make these accusations without evidence.'

'So let's hear your evidence.'

'About the dope that was planted — or the attempt on my life less than an hour ago?'

He did look surprised at that. 'What's that about an attempt on your life?' he demanded.

I told him all that had happened, adding that everything I told him could be corroborated by the speed cop. When I'd finished, he glanced across at Kolowinski and then back to me. 'You've no evidence Franton was involved. Do you intend to make this accusation official?'

I shook my head. 'No, Lieutenant, I don't intend to report this to anyone apart from the two of you. At the moment I want Franton to stay where he is right now. You see, I'm damned sure he killed Edith Somerville's parents and has also made this threat against her — and I'm going to prove it!'

O'Leary looked as if I'd just said something blasphemous. 'Are you completely off your head, Merak? You couldn't make those charges stick no matter how hard you try.'

'Maybe not. But I'm going to have a damned good shot at it. He's already tried to have me jailed on a trumped-up charge. I believe that when that failed, he hired someone to kill me by driving my car off the road hoping it would look like an accident. He's got nothing to lose now and my guess is he'll come for me again. This time, I'll be ready for him.'

O'Leary began tapping his fingers on the desk. Finally, he said, 'You know you're taking a big chance telling me and Kolowinski all of this. I've known Franton for a good many years. My own feelings are that, for some reason, you're paranoid about him. How do you know we won't tell him everything you've just told us? He'd be well within his rights to sue you for what you've just said.'

I grinned. 'You want to know something, Lieutenant? If you were to spill this to him, I don't think he'd even try to get me into a courtroom on a charge of slander or defamation of character. He's too clever for that.'

O'Leary digested that and then pushed himself to his feet. As he moved towards the door, he said, 'I don't intend to say anything of this to Franton and I'm sure the Sergeant here will keep his mouth shut, won't you, Kolowinski?'

The other looked at me and then nodded before following O'Leary out.

Once their footsteps had retreated along the corridor outside, Dawn said softly, 'Was that true about that man trying to force you off the road, Johnny?'

I nodded. 'It's true enough, Dawn. I spotted him right away. He followed me all the way from one of the casinos where I'd met a guy who told me quite a lot about Franton. But more than that he confirmed something I'd always suspected. Herbert Somerville was well in with Carlos Galecci but it seems there was another guy in with them — David Franton!

'Apparently, the three of them had regular meetings and my informant and two other hoods kept a close watch on them. Unfortunately Galecci found out and all three were jailed for ten years on trumped-up drugs and murder charges.'

'You're saying that Franton was in cahoots with Galecci and Edith Somerville's uncle?'

'That's right. Our good cop, as O'Leary calls him, has been working hand in hand with the Organization for years.'

'Then why doesn't this friend of yours go to the police? With this information they could put Franton away for a long time.' She switched on the electric kettle for the afternoon coffee.

'Sure. And how long do you reckon my informant would live if he tried that? About as long as an ice cube in hell.'

'So there isn't much you can do.' Dawn brought the coffee over and put it down in front of me. I lit a cigarette, hoping the coffee would help to clear my head a little. Before I could find out, the phone shrilled. Reaching across the desk, I lifted the receiver.

'Merak,' I said, hoping it wasn't Manzelli demanding answers. It wasn't. It was a woman's voice but it took me several seconds to recognize it as Edith Somerville's. There was a note of hysteria in it that jerked me instantly upright in my chair.

'Can you come quickly, Mister Merak?'

'Where are you?'

'I'm at the family mansion on the outskirts of town. Do you know where it is?'

I told her I did although I didn't mention that Dawn and I had gone out there to shadow her uncle.

'I'm afraid my uncle has been injured. One of the servants apparently heard a shot and found him in his study. I got here as quickly as I could. I think he's still alive but please hurry.'

'I'll be there in twenty minutes,' I said. 'Have you called an ambulance and the cops?'

There was a long pause and then she went on, 'Not yet. I wanted you to be here first.'

That started those little mice careering around inside my mind again. There was something wrong here. But if I was to find out anything I knew I had to get there and ask questions later. I put the phone down and signalled to Dawn. 'Get your coat on.'

'Why? Where are we going?'

'The Somerville place. That was Edith on the phone. It seems her uncle has just been shot but for some reason she wants me there before the cops and ambulance.'

'That's strange.' Dawn muttered the words under her breath as she put on her coat. A couple of minutes later we were in my car and heading for the Somerville place.

The big gates at the end of the long drive swung open as we approached them and I guessed they were operated from somewhere in the house and we'd been seen.

186

Sliding to a halt in front of the large, imposing building, we got out and walked towards the front door. It opened just as I was about to ring the bell.

A tall guy, evidently one of the servants, let us in and led the way along a wide corridor to a room at the far end. Opening the door, he ushered us inside, then left. There were three people in the room — another of the servants standing near the window, Edith Somerville and the guy lying slumped in the chair behind the polished mahogany desk.

'Thank you both for coming so quickly,' Edith said. Her eyes looked red and puffy and I guessed she'd been crying. She gestured towards her uncle. 'This is how he was found. We haven't touched anything.'

I walked over to the desk and bent over Herbert. There was a widening red stain on the front of his white shirt and it was evident he had been shot in the right shoulder. It was impossible to tell the kind of weapon that had been used but from the size of the bullet hole in the silk

I guessed it had been a heavy calibre gun.

I felt his neck. There was a pulse but it was faint and unsteady. Turning to Edith I said harshly. 'You'd better call the cops and the medics now.' She left the room hurriedly. Obviously she didn't want to have her prints all over the phone on the desk. When she'd gone, I addressed the guy at the window. 'I don't suppose you've found any sign of the weapon?'

He shook his head. 'I've checked the room, sir, but there's no sign of any gun although I believe Mister Somerville kept one in the top drawer of his desk.'

Taking out my handkerchief, I wrapped it around my hands and tried the drawer. It was open. As the manservant had said, there was a .38 automatic lying on a bundle of papers. Taking it out, I checked it. It was fully loaded and sniffing it I could tell that it hadn't been fired for some time.

Replacing it, I said, 'Has Mister Somerville had any visitors within the past hour?'

'None that I know of, sir, although I

believe someone did call early this morning.'

'Do you have any idea who it was — man or woman?'

'It was a man. I didn't recognize him as any of the bank employees. Indeed I must confess I didn't like the look of him but it isn't my place to say. But there was an altercation between them. I happened to be in the corridor and heard raised voices.'

'You mean they were quarrelling?'

He paused; then said, 'I would say that, sir.'

'I see. Could you make anything of what they were arguing about?'

'I'm afraid not, sir. I don't listen in to any of the master's conversations.'

I'll bet you don't, I thought.

At that moment, Edith came back into the study. She seemed to have regained some of her composure and sat down when I gestured her to a chair. 'The police and ambulance will be here as quickly as possible,' she said in response to my inquiring look.

Ten minutes later a police car was

speeding along the drive closely followed by the meat wagon. I'd already guessed who the cops would be and, as usually happened, I was right. Lieutenant O'Leary came in with Sergeant Kolowinski at his shoulder.

Close behind came two medics. They both moved towards the desk, then halted as O'Leary said sharply, 'Don't touch anything until I've had a look at him.'

'Better be quick then, Lieutenant,' said one of the guys. 'He's losing blood and the sooner we get him to the hospital, the better his chances. It's possible the slug has punctured his lung.'

'I'll only be a couple of minutes,' O'Leary said testily. He unbuttoned Somerville's shirt and drew it away from the flesh. 'A heavy calibre weapon,' he said. I couldn't say whether he was speaking to himself or Kolowinski

Straightening up, he nodded to the two medics. 'All right. Get him to the hospital. I'll need to have everything in this room dusted for prints. In the meantime,' he swung on the rest of us, 'I'm not surprised to see you here at the crime scene, Merak. You're always where you're least wanted. Now, who found him?'

The manservant spoke up. 'I did, Lieutenant. I heard what sounded like a shot and came in to find him slumped in his chair. I immediately telephoned the Ocean View Hotel and the receptionist said she'd inform Miss Edith immediately. She came about ten minutes later.'

O'Leary swung to face me. 'And just where do you come in on this, Merak?'

'I called him and asked him to come,' Edith interjected.

'I see. And was that before, or after, you phoned us? I'd advise you not to lie to us, Miss Somerville. The way we get across town, we'd have got here some time before he did if you'd phoned us first.'

'Then why ask the question if you already know the answer,' I said.

I could see he didn't like that for he snapped, 'I'm questioning Miss Somerville, Merak. I'll come to you next.'

While he took her to one side, Kolowinski sidled over to me. In a low voice, he asked, 'What do you make of this, Johnny? You figure this is the work of one of the mobs?'

'I thought it was at first,' I told him. 'Now I'm not so sure. The guys who carry out the orders of the Big Boys are all professionals. From what I saw, Somerville was a sitting target yet the slug just hit him in the right shoulder, nowhere near the heart.'

The Sergeant considered that, rubbing his chin. 'I see what you mean. It's almost as if they didn't intend to kill him.'

'That would make some kind of sense,' I agreed. 'Maybe he stepped out of line and this was just a warning.'

I ran that idea past O'Leary when he began to question me a few minutes later. 'You seem damned sure he was linked to the Organization,' he said, watching me closely.

'I've never been more sure of anything in my life.'

Nodding, he closed his notebook and thrust it back into his pocket. 'All right. Merak. That's it for now. I may want to question some of you later so don't be taking any unexpected visits out of town.'

I walked over to where Edith was sitting in the chair near the window. 'Would you like a lift back into town?' I asked. 'There isn't much more you can do here.'

'Thank you, I'd appreciate that.' She got up and followed Dawn and I outside. I knew what she was thinking. The person who had shot her uncle could well be the one who was threatening her life — a life that was growing shorter with every passing day. This incident might be a warning that not even the police, not even Johnny Merak, could do anything to prevent her death in a few days time.

8

The Last Rose

Three days passed. I'd arrived at the office early that morning. Dawn wouldn't be in for another hour so I'd poured myself a stiff drink and was sipping it slowly, trying to put my thoughts into some kind of order. If I was right, Edith Somerville would have received four roses this morning; four short days of hell for her and I was still no closer to getting a real break in the hunt for this sadistic killer.

I'd made a few discreet inquiries about Franton but there seemed to be nothing to tie him to the attempt on Herbert Somerville's life. Knowing him, however, I guessed that most of those men under him were scared to say anything against him. They'd have said he was in the office at the time of the shooting when in reality he'd been absent.

Over the past three days I'd tried to get into the hospital ward to talk with Somerville and each time I'd been told he was too ill to see anyone. I'd asked the doctors and nurses about him but, for some strange reason, it was as if someone had built a wall of silence around him. I checked my watch. It was almost eight thirty. Another half hour before I could expect Dawn to arrive. I decided to have another go at the hospital and this time I decided to use a different means of getting to Somerville.

I got there less than fifteen minutes later. I'd figured this would be a quiet time and, as I'd hoped, there was no one at the reception desk. Slipping past it I went along a corridor, which, as I knew from previous visits, led to the private wing of the hospital. There was only one person in sight when I got there — a young woman pushing a trolley loaded with food. She looked startled to see me but soon recovered her composure.

Before she could say anything, I said quietly, 'I've been told at the desk that Herbert Somerville is in one of these private rooms. Could you tell me which it is?'

The fact that I'd mentioned the reception desk seemed to put her at her ease for she replied, 'Certainly. It's that one over there.' She pointed towards the door opposite where I was standing.

After thanking her, I went over to the door in question and opened it quietly. Somerville was lying in the bed next to the window. He didn't look too good, his eyes half open and most of the color gone from his face. He turned his head slowly as I entered, closing the door behind me.

'How are you getting on?' I asked softly. 'Have they got that slug out of your chest?'

Running his tongue around his lips, he muttered, 'What the hell are you doing here, Merak? I gave orders that no one was to come here.'

'So I've discovered. The trouble is, I take very little notice of any orders I'm given. All I want to know is whether you saw who shot you.'

He shook his head. 'I saw nothing. I was busy writing.'

'But you must have seen something,' I persisted.

'I've just told you. I saw nothing.'

'Didn't you even hear someone come into the room?'

'If I did, I'd take no notice. The servants are always coming in and out. All I know is that there was a shot. I felt the slug hit me and the next thing I remember is waking up in this bed. Now get the hell out of here before I call an orderly and have you thrown out.'

I held up my hands. 'All right, Mister Somerville, I'm going. But if you do remember anything, I'd be grateful if you'd let me know.'

He twisted his lips into a scowl. 'If I do remember anything, Merak, I'll give the information to the police, not to you.'

'Suit yourself,' I said. I let myself out. A tall guy in a white coat passed me. He gave me a funny look but said nothing. He was still staring after me as I passed through the entrance and walked back to my car. I'd hoped to get a bit more out of Somerville but it was evident he wasn't talking. Clearly, he had a lot to hide and was scared. That would make him determined to keep it all to himself.

Once inside the office, I poured myself a second drink before Dawn arrived. It helped to clear my head. Then I ran through the list of suspects. Malloy's gang was still in my sights even though he was dead but his death put anyone else in that outfit at the bottom of my list of suspects. My guess about that killing was that Malloy had been killed by someone wanting his place as head of the gang.

There was Herbert Somerville who had been tied in with the Organization for a number of years. He could easily have arranged for someone to shoot him in the shoulder hoping to divert suspicion from himself. It was a drastic action but then these people were playing for high stakes.

Then there was David Franton, the relative latecomer on the scene. His involvement with both the Mob and Edith Somerville provided him with a very strong motive for murder. It was going to be a process of elimination but before I could get very far, Dawn came in. She looked surprised to see me.

'You're early today, Johnny,' she said. 'What's wrong? Did you have a bad night?'

'Something like that,' I admitted. 'This case has got me stymied. There are so many things about it that don't add up.' I sat back in my chair. 'I went along to the hospital to see if I could have a word with Herbert Somerville.'

'And did you?'

'I got into his room but he wasn't very talkative. He admitted someone came into his study but he said he didn't bother to look up to check who it was. He reckoned it was just one of the servants. The next thing he remembers is lying in the hospital bed.'

'But you think he's lying?'

'Of course he's lying. My guess is he got someone to put that bullet in him. That's why he's not talking.'

Dawn looked surprised by that remark. 'You mean he deliberately asked someone to shoot him? Why would he do that?'

'To divert any suspicion from himself.

It was little more than a flesh wound and I've no doubt he was feigning unconsciousness when we arrived on the scene.'

'You think he could be the man we're after, the one responsible for these murders?'

Nodding, I said, 'I reckon it's either him or Franton. I certainly hope it isn't anyone from the Organization. A lot of nasty things are likely to happen if you start poking around in their affairs.'

At that moment, the phone rang. There was an impatient ring to it as though whoever was on the other end of the line wanted to talk urgently to me. I guessed it was either O'Leary or possibly Edith but it was neither.

A voice I didn't recognize said, 'Is that Johnny Merak, the private investigator?'

'The same,' I replied. 'Just who is this?'

'Listen. I've only got a couple of minutes to talk. I reckon I have some information that could be useful.'

'All right. Let's have it.' I figured that, for some reason, he wanted to remain anonymous.

'I can't talk over the phone. If you want

it, you'll have to come here. But first you'll need to get the warden's permission.'

'The warden's permission?' It took a full minute for that to sink it. 'You mean you're in jail. So what kind of information do you have? Is it anything to do with the Somerville murders?'

Something like a dry chuckle sounded from the other end of the line. 'Now you're catching on, Merak. I'm on a twenty-year holiday in San Quentin. If you want to know what I've got, just get here and ask for Frederick Donner. I'll be waiting.' The line went dead.

Dawn brought my coffee over and said, 'What was all that about, Johnny?'

'It seems this case has even reached the inmates of San Quentin. That was one of the prisoners there, some guy named Frederick Donner. He reckons he's got some important information that he wants to give me.'

'And are you going? It seems unlikely to me that anyone in jail will know anything of importance about this case. Have you ever heard of this guy?'

I shook my head. 'No. But unfortunately, I can't afford to pass up any possible lead. At the moment there are so many blind alleys in this case that I'm stumbling through it like a blind man without a white stick. If there's any chance at all that this guy knows something important, then I'll have to go and talk to him. But first I'll have to get the warden's permission.'

'Is he likely to give it?'

'That depends on whether he remembers me from the three years I spent there before I pulled out of the Organization.' Reaching for the phone directory I soon got the number for San Quentin prison and within five minutes had the warden on the other end of the line. He listened while I put my request to him, then said, 'May I ask what this is all about, Mister Merak?' If he remembered my name from my stay in the slammer he gave no sign of it. Maybe he hadn't been warden there while I'd done my time.

'Certainly. I'm working on a murder case at the moment and I received a phone call from an inmate calling himself

Frederick Donner. He told me he had some very important information concerning this case but he couldn't tell me over the phone. I'd have to see him face to face.'

There was a pause while the other considered that. I figured he must have believed what I said for he went on, 'Very well. I can see no reason why you shouldn't speak to him. But I must confess I can't see what help he can be in your investigation. However, I'll make all of the necessary arrangements at this end. Just give your name when you arrive.'

* * *

The sight of those walls at San Quentin brought back painful memories as I parked the car and walked up to the gate. I knew that if it hadn't been for Harry Grenville and Dawn I'd probably have spent the greater part of my life behind them. It wasn't a pleasant feeling.

Once inside, I gave my name to the warder. He glanced at his clipboard, then ticked my name and told me to follow him. Here, inside those gates, even more memories came flooding back. I tried to push them from my mind but it wasn't easy. Once you've had a taste of the penitentiary it never leaves you.

My companion took me along a narrow corridor, unlocking each door in turn and locking them again behind us. Finally, we reached a large room, divided down the middle by a row of bars. There was a chair in front of them and I could see another chair on the other side. At the moment, it was empty.

I had only just sat down when a door opened and this guy came through. He was dressed in prison clothes and was handcuffed. There were two men with him and one of them pushed him into the chair.

'All right, Donner,' I said. 'You asked for this meeting so I'm here. Just what is it you've got to say? Before you do, I want to make it clear I'm not here to cut any deals for you. If your information proves of any help, I'm willing to testify to that at any parole board, but that's all.'

If he felt disappointed at that, he didn't

show it. In fact, there was no expression at all on his wrinkled features.

'Three years ago I worked at the Marsden Hotel. I was there on the night that George Somerville fell from that window. The talk in here is that you believe it was murder and not suicide as the cops figured. Also you've got Franton, a Lieutenant in the Drugs Squad as a possible suspect.'

'I don't know how you know all of this,' I said.

He twisted his thin lips in what was supposed to be a smile. 'You'd be surprised how quickly news spreads in a place like this.'

'Not really. I spent three years in here so nothing you tell me comes as any surprise. But you're right. He is at the top of my list of suspects.'

He leaned forward a little, placing his elbows on his knees. 'I don't know what evidence you've got linking Franton to any other murders but where George Somerville is concerned, he's not your killer.'

I experienced a sudden sense of

surprise. This was something I hadn't expected to hear.

'No? So how do you know that?'

'I was waiting on the tables that particular evening and I was able to pick up quite a bit of the talk. There were several guys there from the gangs and I figured it was strange that a cop should be on such friendly terms with these mobsters. So I kept him in my sights all the time. I reckoned if I could get something on him it might come in useful in the future.'

'You mean blackmail?'

He smiled again. 'Why not? A crooked cop is always good for a few thousand bucks if you know how to go about it.'

'So what you're telling me is that when Somerville left the room after probably having his drink spiked, Franton was still in the room right up to when the body was discovered.'

He nodded. 'That's exactly what I'm telling you, Merak. Whoever pushed Somerville out of that window, it certainly wasn't Franton.'

I thought that over for a moment. I'd

no reason to believe Donner was lying. Finally, I said, 'Even though this proves Franton wasn't the actual murderer, he could've paid someone to do the job for him.'

Donner shook his head. 'That isn't how Franton works. He prefers to do things himself. I reckon he gets some kind of kick from inflicting pain on others.'

After what had happened to me earlier at Franton's hands, I knew that was true.

A couple of minutes later, I got up and left. As I moved away, the two guys with Donner grabbed his arms and led him out of the room. Over his shoulder, he called harshly, 'You won't forget. If I ever do get a parole hearing, you'll put in a word for me, Mister Merak?'

'I won't forget,' I called back.

Standing outside the prison in the sunlight that Donner wouldn't see for several more years, I felt more confused than before. I'd been sure that Franton had killed George Somerville three years before. Now I had to rethink everything, always assuming that Donner had told me the truth. I couldn't think of any reason why he should be lying. If Franton had been responsible in any way for putting him inside, his natural reaction would surely be to try and implicate him in the murder rather than give him an alibi.

I drove back to the office with those little mice turning cartwheels inside my head. There now seemed to be several possibilities. The one candidate I'd figured had motive, means and opportunity had been eliminated by what Donner had just told me.

★　★　★

It was early in the afternoon two days later when I got the break I'd been waiting for. I'd spent almost every minute going over all of the details I had, searching almost frantically for some clue that might point me in the right direction. I'd found nothing. The one thought that dominated everything in my mind was that tomorrow Edith Somerville would receive the final rose and, if that note meant what it said, meet her Maker.

It wasn't a very pleasant thought. I'd

already made up my mind that the next day I wouldn't let Edith out of my sight just in case anyone did try anything. I guess O'Leary also had that thought on his mind for he called at least twice every day asking if I'd gotten any further with the case.

Dawn had gone out for a couple of sandwiches and we were both eating them when there was a knock on the door. It was a polite kind of knock, not the hard business kind that O'Leary used when he came and it was the last person I expected to see — Lieutenant Franton!

He gave Dawn a brief glance, then stepped forward and sat down in the chair opposite me. There was an almost apologetic expression on his hard features that surprised me.

'You're here with another warrant, Lieutenant?' I asked. 'If you are I'm afraid we still don't have any drugs on the premises.'

'Actually I'm here to return your gun and also to explain certain things which are not to go beyond this office.' He gave Dawn another piercing look.

'It's all right, Lieutenant. You can speak freely in front of my assistant.'

Handing the Luger across the desk he went on, 'I'm sorry about the affair with the cocaine but at the time I was in a very sticky position. I had the impression you were trying to pin a double murder on me and spill everything about my association with the Mobs.'

'And, of course, you're completely innocent on both charges.'

'That's why I'm here now. I believe you've been to San Quentin to interview one of the inmates there — Frederick Donner.'

'That's right.' I gave a quick nod, wondering what was coming next. It wasn't what I expected.

'And no doubt he told you about my presence at that meeting when George Somerville died and that I was in the room during the whole time it happened.'

'He did.'

Staring straight ahead, he said, 'I don't suppose you're aware that the Mobs have been bringing in large supplies of illegal drugs into the country via Mexico. For the past five years I've been working undercover until now I've gained their confidence to the point where I'm ready to move in on the Big Boys behind this operation.

'Since you've been working with both the Feds and the Organization you were becoming a danger to everything I'd built up over the past five years. I couldn't let that happen and I had to figure a way of getting you off my back — at least for a little while.'

'So you decided to frame me for handling drugs. And when that didn't work you sent one of your boys after me to drive me off the road.' I noticed the expression of surprise that flashed across his features.

'Believe me, Merak, that wasn't any of my doing. I may have a reputation for beating up suspects when they refuse to cooperate but I stop short of murder.'

For some strange reason, I believed him. Franton might be a sadistic cop when it came to extracting information from crooks who didn't want to talk, but I couldn't see him as a cold-blooded killer.

'All right,' I said finally. 'Somehow, I reckon you're telling the truth. Which means I'm nowhere nearer discovering the identity of this murderer than when I started this investigation. Now you've told me all this I'll stay out of your hair as far as the Organization is concerned.'

'Thanks.' He got up. 'And please remember, not a word of this to anyone.'

Once he'd gone, Dawn said in a disappointed tone, 'Assuming that Franton and this jailbird are both telling the truth, we're left with only one conclusion. Someone in the Mobs is responsible for these murders. And that means it could be anyone.'

'Not really. We still have two possible killers — Herbert Somerville and Malloy. They were both in something together and from what I know of them they're both capable of murder.'

'But Malloy's dead,' Dawn protested.

'Sure — he's dead and if it was him, he'll never face the chair.'

I sat back in my chair as another idea struck me. Was it possible that Malloy had been the Mister Big bringing all of these drugs into the country, the man Franton was after? If he had been the one, then maybe Somerville wanted a part of the action and was willing to fund the deals in return for a share of the profits. The more I thought about it, the more sense it made. It was also possible that Mrs. Somerville had somehow found out about the deal and had to be eliminated.

But where did Edith fit into all of this? Had she also found out and Malloy's twisted, sadistic mind had conjured up this bizarre means of getting her out of the picture? Everything seemed to slot together perfectly except that Malloy's sudden and unexpected demise now posed an important question. If it had been Malloy did his death mean there was no longer a threat against her? Yet those little mice were telling me there was something important that I'd overlooked.

I knew that Dawn had been watching me closely. Now she said, 'You've obviously got something on your mind, Johnny. What is it?'

I went over the theory I'd been running

through my mind. I knew if there were any flaws in it she'd spot them right away. She listened in silence until I'd finished, then nodded. 'It seems logical to me,' she said at last. 'But I can tell from that look on your face that there's something else troubling you.'

Lighting a cigarette I drew deeply on it hoping it would focus my mind on what had been bothering me for some time. Just what was it I was trying to remember?

Then, right out of nowhere, it came to me.

Leaning forward over the desk, I said harshly, 'My God, Dawn, we've been on the wrong track from the very beginning. It's been staring me in the face all this time but I've been too stupid to recognize it.'

Dawn looked puzzled. 'I don't see what you're getting at, Johnny.'

'When I asked Jack Kolowinski about George Somerville's apparent suicide he told me he'd been in that room half an hour after it happened. He said there were marks on the carpet just in front of the window as if there'd been some kind of struggle.

'There was also a small tear in the material. I didn't take much notice of it at the time. But my guess is that small tear is telling us something important.'

'What?' Dawn asked, still puzzled.

'That it could have been made by a pair of high heels.'

Dawn stared at me as if I'd just lost my marbles. 'Are you telling me you believe it was a woman who heaved George Somerville out of that window?'

'Why not? I'll lay any bet that you could.'

She bit her lower lip. 'Well yes, I suppose I could. But what motive would Edith Somerville have to kill her own father?'

Stubbing out my cigarette, I said, 'My guess is that those psychiatrists are right. We're dealing with someone who's completely insane, a psychopathic killer — but someone who's also very clever. After all, the dividing line between genius and madness is extremely thin. She's had me fooled all along the line. Spinning me that yarn on the train. There never was a threat against her life. Those roses that came every morning were just part of a very clever plot to throw me completely off the scent.

'All this time she's been playing the part of the victim while this burning hatred of the Organization and all it stands for sent her on this killing spree. She evidently believed both her father and mother were giving large sums of money to the Mobs so they had to be eliminated. The same goes for her uncle. She definitely meant to kill him and I've no doubt that she killed Malloy and she'll finish the job on her uncle and then Franton is the next one she'll go after unless we can stop her.'

'This is all very hard to believe,' Dawn sounded dubious. 'And to be honest, I can't see how you're going to prove any of this. I'm sure O'Leary won't go for it.'

'I agree. That's going to be the difficult bit. She's far too clever not to have covered her tracks completely. If it wasn't for this murderous streak she'd have made a top dramatic actress in Holly-wood.'

'So you reckon she's going to get away with it?'

'Not if I can help it. I'll think of something before tomorrow. No one's going to make a fool of Johnny Merak and get away with it.' I tried to sound confident but it wasn't easy.

★ ★ ★

The next day I arrived early at the office and put through a call to Lieutenant O'Leary. I asked him to meet me at the Ocean View Hotel. He didn't sound too keen but eventually he agreed. After scribbling a note and leaving it on Dawn's desk, I went down to where the Merc stood waiting. It took me twenty minutes to drive through the early morning traffic to the Ocean View Hotel.

There was no one in the foyer when I arrived. Then the door to one side of the desk opened and the receptionist came through. She seemed surprised to see me standing there but she recognized me at once.

'Were you looking for someone, Mister Merak?' she inquired.

'I came to have a word with Edith Somerville,' I told her. 'But at the moment she doesn't seem to be anywhere around.'

'She may be at breakfast. I'll check if she's in the dining room.' She went out and returned a couple of minutes later, shaking her head. 'She's probably up in her room. Would you like me to contact her and let her know you're here?'

'That won't be necessary,' I said. 'I'm expecting Lieutenant O'Leary and Sergeant Kolowinski of the LAPD any minute. The Lieutenant may want to speak to her in her room.'

Five minutes later there was the sound of a car outside and then O'Leary came in followed by the Sergeant. They walked right up to me.

'All right, Merak, What's this all about? Whatever it is, it had better be good.'

'I brought you here to meet our killer face to face, Lieutenant,' I said soberly. 'It took me quite a while to figure it all out and even now I can scarcely believe it.'

He looked puzzled. Then his expression turned to one of incredulous disbelief. 'You mean Edith Somerville? You're completely on the wrong track now, Merak.'

'In a way I hope I am but it's the only thing that makes any sense as far as I'm concerned. Perhaps you'd like to come with me to her room.'

I could see he still didn't believe me but he accompanied me up the winding staircase to the top floor where I paused outside Edith's door. I knocked. There was no answer.

'It would seem there's no one at home,' Kolowinski observed.

O'Leary stared directly at me. 'I hope you're not going to suggest that we break down the door,' he said sharply. 'And don't ask me to get a search warrant to back up your stupid idea. There isn't a judge who'd grant one and — '

He broke off at the sound of someone coming up the stairs. A moment later, Edith Somerville appeared at the end of the corridor. I saw her hesitate the moment she spotted us. Then she came towards us. She was holding a key and a handbag in one hand and a single rose in the other.

'Were you looking for me, Lieutenant?' she asked in a low voice, barely more than a whisper. Turning to look at me, she held out the rose. 'The last one, Mister Merak. And you still haven't found whoever is threatening to kill me.'

'I'm afraid you're wrong, Miss Somerville,' I replied. 'I know exactly who sent you that note and has been sending you these roses over the past fortnight.'

Something changed in her expression but it was gone almost instantly. 'Then I suppose you'd better come in and tell me.' She unlocked the door and led us into the room where she remained standing near the door. 'Now what is it you have to tell me?'

'You wrote that note, just as you've been sending these roses to yourself. Every morning you'd slip out of the hotel, buy the exact number you needed and put them on the reception desk with your name on a note attached to them.'

Her lips twisted as she glared at me. 'That's ridiculous. You'll never be able to prove that,' she snapped.

'Possibly not with all of the others,' I replied. 'But you gave yourself away with the one you're now holding in your hand.' I dug inside my jacket and pulled out a single rose. 'You see, this is the one you bought this morning. I took it from the reception desk when I first got here, together with the note you attached to it. I reckon you must have been in a panic when you went downstairs to find it gone. You had to get another to replace it and since you had very little time there was only one place you could get one — out there in the hotel garden. I think that if we were to take a good look around we'd find the bush where one has been recently snipped off.'

'All right. So I'm guilty of sending flowers to myself and wasting police time. But you can't pin these murders on me.' Her voice had risen in pitch and there was a look on her face and in her eyes I'd never seen before.

'Oh, but I think I can. It all began when your father died. It was made to look like suicide but we now know it was murder. He was drugged at that meeting in the Marsden Hotel and heaved over the window ledge. In his semi-conscious state he couldn't put up much of a fight with his killer.

'There was a small tear in the carpet near the window, one made by someone wearing high-heeled shoes. There were only two women present at that meeting — you and your mother. Whether your mother could've heaved him out of the window I'm not sure but I'm quite certain you could. The final clincher as far as I'm concerned is that you're the only one who was anywhere in the vicinity when all of these murders were committed. When your uncle was shot the servant said he phoned the Ocean View Hotel and spoke to the receptionist. Yet you arrived on the scene ten minutes later. It would've been impossible for you to drive from the Ocean View to the mansion in such a short time. My guess is you were somewhere in the house at that time.'

Something must have snapped in Edith's mind at that moment. Before any of us could move she'd opened the handbag and thrust her hand inside. When it emerged it was holding a gun.

'You've been just a little too clever, Mister Merak,' she snarled. There was no longer any doubt in my mind that the psychiatrists had been right. She was no longer the meek, frightened woman I'd met on the train. She looked like the Devil Incarnate.

'Put that gun down, Miss Somerville,' O'Leary said. 'There's no doubt you need proper professional help and we'll see that you get it. But if you pull that trigger you'll get the chair or — '

'Don't come any closer. If only that hoodlum I paid to drive you off the road had done his job right I'd never have been found out.'

'So you were trying to add me to your list of victims even then?'

'Of course. You were getting a little too close to the truth.'

She pointed the weapon at me and I

thought I saw her finger tighten on the trigger. I was staring the Grim Reaper in the face and there was nothing I could do about it.

Then, without any warning, the door behind her was thrust open, hurling her forward, off balance. The gun slipped from her fingers. Dawn came in. She must have taken in everything within a split second. Edith had pushed herself to her feet and was lunging for the gun when Dawn grabbed her arm and pulled her upright. The next second she was flying across the room, hitting the wall with a thud that could have been heard in the basement.

Reaching down, I picked up the gun and handed it to the Lieutenant who seemed to be having trouble believing what he'd just witnessed. Swallowing hard, he said, 'I reckon you came in just in time, Miss Grahame. It seems we've had a maniac in our midst and never realized it.'

He turned to Kolowinski. 'You'd better cuff her, Sergeant before she comes round and then take her down to the precinct.'

When they'd gone, O'Leary said, 'Was she responsible for all of these murders and the attempted murder of Herbert Somerville?'

'She was, including Malloy and his three boys at the beach place. I'd already figured that wasn't a gang killing. It had to be someone they knew and who posed no threat to them. When Edith turned up they probably figured she was there on behalf of her uncle and had come to talk.

'Unfortunately for them that wasn't her intention at all. My guess is she used a silencer and they were all dead before they knew what was happening. One other thing I noticed. There were tire tracks in the sand close to the beach house. But from the depth of them I knew they weren't made by a heavy car like those used by the gangs. It had to be something like the car Edith drove.'

'And her motive?' Kolowinski asked.

'I think that all began with Franton. She clearly believed he was an upright law officer when she first met him. Then some of his sadistic nature started to show and once she discovered he was in with

Galecci, it was the finish. It's possible she was always mentally unbalanced but that drove her right over the edge. She should have been put in an institution a long time ago but like some psychos she was also very clever at hiding her feelings.'

'And that charade with the roses?' O'Leary asked.

'Only a deranged mind could have thought that one up. Somehow, I don't think she'll face a trial for first-degree murder. You saw how she changed once she knew I'd figured everything out. My guess is she'll spend the rest of her life in a padded cell.'

Dawn looked at O'Leary. 'Can Johnny and I go now, Lieutenant?'

O'Leary hesitated, then he shrugged. 'Okay, you can for now. I can collect your statements later.'

'Glad to be of service, Lieutenant,' I said, and took Dawn's arm.

As we walked down the stairs together I could sense that O'Leary would be scowling daggers after me.

Later, when Dawn and I returned to the office, she asked, 'What are you going to do about Manzelli, Johnny? I think he should know how things have turned out.'

I thought that over. It was true that without Manzelli's protection I might never have solved the case. 'You're right, of course, Dawn. He probably knows much of it but I'll give him as many of the details as I can.'

'And Franton's undercover work inside the Organization?'

'I think I'll keep quiet about that for the moment. There's no reason he should find out about it from me.'

Dawn nodded, then she gave an odd smile.

'Something on your mind?' I asked.

'You know,' she said, 'I suppose, in a way, she was right all the time. You could say that her life has ended today with that last rose.'

I couldn't have put it better myself!

THE END

We do hope that you have enjoyed reading this large print book.

Did you know that all of our titles are available for purchase?

We publish a wide range of high quality large print books including:
Romances, Mysteries, Classics
General Fiction
Non Fiction and Westerns

Special interest titles available in large print are:
The Little Oxford Dictionary
Music Book, Song Book
Hymn Book, Service Book

Also available from us courtesy of Oxford University Press:
Young Readers' Dictionary
(large print edition)
Young Readers' Thesaurus
(large print edition)

For further information or a free brochure, please contact us at:
Ulverscroft Large Print Books Ltd.,
The Green, Bradgate Road, Anstey,
Leicester, LE7 7FU, England.
Tel: (00 44) **0116 236 4325**
Fax: (00 44) **0116 234 0205**

FERAL

Steve Hayes & David Whitehead

There's something not quite right about Shelby's Oasis, the tourist trap in the middle of the Arizona desert. The Shelby sisters, Agnes and Diana, have more skeletons than closets in which to hide them. And with rumours of a fortune in gold buried on the property, who can be trusted — the sisters' scheming brother Scott? The seductive Kelly-Anne? Or Mitch, the loner who stumbles into their lives? One thing's for sure: nothing at Shelby's Oasis is what it seems . . .

THE RED INSECTS

John Russell Fearn

Nick Hansley, his wife Ena and father-in-law find that their country house, 'The Cedars', radiates a positively evil aura. Their strange neighbour Dr. Lexton calls, wanting to buy their home. But who is Dr. Lexton? And as for Ena's deceased uncle, entomologist Cyrus Odder, what was the nature of the secret experiment he had worked on there? Then after a mysterious death in the house — death spreads its net across the countryside — and the entire world . . .

DEAD END

Steve Hayes & David Whitehead

Dead End, Arizona, was just another whistle-stop on the way to nowhere. But in Dead End the future of humanity depended upon the actions of a few brave souls . . . and an army of supernatural creatures with no souls at all! Earth could be invaded by another planet if they lost the war — but if they won, the battle between the living and the undead would continue . . . Either way, the streets of Dead End were going to run with blood.

FIFTY DAYS TO DOOM

E. C. Tubb

The galaxy is at war between the oxygen-breathing Terran Federation of worlds and the Ginzoes, chlorine-breathing aliens. An Earth ship is captured in battle by the Ginzoes, and its crew learns that the aliens have a newly developed catalyst. This can liberate chlorine from the sea — which, for the Ginzoes, would convert Terran worlds into suitable environments. The catalyst will be used unless the Terran Federation declares peace within fifty days. Fifty days to save Mankind . . . or fifty days to doom!

THE GOLD OF AKADA

John Russell Fearn

When Harry Perrivale wanted to find the legendary lost city of Akada, his expedition to the African jungle included his native bearers, his wife Rita and trader Caleb Moon. But Harry faced mortal danger as Moon had his own dark plans for the treasures of Akada. Then they confronted a mysterious giant white man, who spoke only in a native tribal tongue. His identity and the reason for his jungle upbringing would only be discovered after tragedy struck . . .